Problem Solvers

Edited by L. Marder
Senior Lecturer in Mathematics, Universi

No. 8

Matrices and Vector Spaces

Problem Solvers

1. ORDINARY DIFFERENTIAL EQUATIONS—J. Heading
2. CALCULUS OF SEVERAL VARIABLES—L. Marder
3. VECTOR ALGEBRA—L. Marder
4. ANALYTICAL MECHANICS—D. F. Lawden
5. CALCULUS OF ONE VARIABLE—K. Hirst
6. COMPLEX NUMBERS—J. Williams
7. VECTOR FIELDS—L. Marder
8. MATRICES AND VECTOR SPACES—F. Brickell

Matrices and Vector Spaces

F. BRICKELL
Senior Lecturer in Mathematics,
University of Southampton

LONDON GEORGE ALLEN & UNWIN LTD
RUSKIN HOUSE   MUSEUM STREET

ISBN 0 04 512016 1 hardback
    0 04 512017 × paper

Printed in Great Britain
in 10 on 12 pt 'Monophoto' Times Mathematics Series 569
by Page Bros (Norwich) Ltd., Norwich

Contents

1. THE ALGEBRA OF MATRICES page
1.1 Introduction 1
1.2 The addition of matrices 1
1.3 The multiplication of matrices 2
1.4 Scalar multiplication of a matrix 6
1.5 Partitioned matrices 7
1.6 The transposition of matrices 9
1.7 Complex matrices 11

2 THE DETERMINANT OF A SQUARE MATRIX
2.1 Permutations 14
2.2 The definition of a determinant 14
2.3 Properties of a determinant 16
2.4 Cofactors and the inverse of a square matrix 19

3 ELEMENTARY TRANSFORMATIONS OF A MATRIX
3.1 Elementary transformations and linear equations 27
3.2 The rank of a matrix 29
3.3 Elementary matrices 32

4 LINEAR TRANSFORMATIONS
4.1 Eigenvalues and eigenvectors 38
4.2 Orthogonal and unitary matrices 42
4.3 Orthogonal transformations of real quadratic forms 47
4.4 Matrix polynomials 49

5 REAL QUADRATIC FORMS
5.1 The rank and index of a real quadratic form 55
5.2 The simultaneous reduction of real quadratic forms 58

6 VECTOR SPACES
6.1 Definition 64
6.2 Linear dependence 65
6.3 Linear mappings 68
6.4 Linear operators 71
6.5 Euclidean vector spaces 74
6.6 Unitary vector spaces 77
6.7 The Jordan normal form 79

ANSWERS TO EXERCISES 84

INDEX 87

Chapter 1

The Algebra of Matrices

1.1 Introduction A *matrix* is a rectangular array of numbers such as

$$\begin{bmatrix} 1 & 3 & 1 \\ 0 & -2 & 2 \end{bmatrix} \quad \text{or} \quad \begin{bmatrix} -3 & 0 \\ 1 & 2 \end{bmatrix}$$

The first matrix has 2 rows and 3 columns and we say that it has *order* 2 by 3. This is written as 2×3 but no multiplication is implied! The second matrix is of order 2×2 and is an example of a *square matrix*.

We use a capital letter, perhaps A, for a matrix and then use a_{ij} for the element in the ith row and jth column of A. A is also denoted by $[a_{ij}]$. The numbers a_{ij} will be assumed to be real or complex numbers and the matrix will be called correspondingly a *real* or *complex matrix*. Matrices with just one row or column are known as *row* or *column vectors* respectively. Two matrices $[a_{ij}]$ and $[b_{ij}]$ are said to be *equal* if and only if they have the same order and $a_{ij} = b_{ij}$ for all values of i and j.

Matrices are used to simplify the calculations which arise, for example, when linear equations are solved or when linear changes of coordinates are made. This use requires operations called addition and multiplication of matrices.

1.2 The Addition of Matrices The *sum* of two matrices is defined only for matrices of the same order. The definition is $[a_{ij}] + [b_{ij}] = [a_{ij} + b_{ij}]$.

Problem 1.1 Calculate $F + G$ where

$$F = \begin{bmatrix} 1 & 3 \\ 0 & -2 \end{bmatrix}, \quad G = \begin{bmatrix} -6 & 4 \\ 1 & 2 \end{bmatrix}.$$

Solution. The sum is defined and is the matrix

$$\begin{bmatrix} 1+(-6) & 3+4 \\ 0+1 & -2+2 \end{bmatrix} = \begin{bmatrix} -5 & 7 \\ 1 & 0 \end{bmatrix}. \qquad \square$$

A matrix with all its elements zero is called a *zero matrix* and we denote it by O. There is a zero matrix of any order. If A is any matrix and O is the zero matrix of the same order $A + O = A$.

The *negative* of the matrix $A = [a_{ij}]$ is the matrix $[-a_{ij}]$ and it is denoted by $-A$. It is obvious that $A+(-A) = 0$. The negative is used to define the *subtraction* of two matrices by $A-B = A+(-B)$.

The addition of matrices is commutative, that is $A+B = B+A$. It is also associative, that is $(A+B)+C = A+(B+C)$.

Problem 1.2 Detail the steps involved in solving the equation $X+F = G$ where F and G are the matrices in Problem 1.1.

Solution. From $X+F = G$ we obtain $(X+F)+(-F) = G+(-F) = G-F$, and, using the associative law, $X+(F+(-F)) = G-F$. Therefore $X+0 = G-F$ and consequently

$$X = G-F = \begin{bmatrix} -7 & 1 \\ 1 & 4 \end{bmatrix}. \qquad \square$$

1.3 The Multiplication of Matrices   We begin with the product of row and column vectors

$$X = [x_1 \ldots x_n], \qquad Y = \begin{bmatrix} y_1 \\ \vdots \\ y_n \end{bmatrix}$$

which have the same number of elements. XY is defined to be the 1×1 matrix $[x_1 y_1 + \ldots + x_n y_n]$.

In general the product AB of two matrices is defined only if the number of columns in A is the same as the number of rows in B. To define the product we think of A and B as made up of row and column vectors respectively. Then the element in the ith row and jth column of AB is the element in the product of the ith row of A with the jth column of B. If A is of order $r \times s$ and B is of order $s \times t$ then AB is of order $r \times t$.

Problem 1.3   Calculate the element in the 3rd row and 2nd column of the product AB where

$$A = \begin{bmatrix} 4 & 1 \\ 0 & 3 \\ 7 & 8 \end{bmatrix}, \qquad B = \begin{bmatrix} 2 & 5 \\ 6 & 9 \end{bmatrix}.$$

Solution. The product AB is defined (although BA is not). The required element is the element in the product of the 3rd row of A with the 2nd column of B. It is therefore $(7)(5)+(8)(9) = 107$. $\qquad \square$

Problem 1.4 A and B are matrices such that AB and BA are both defined. What are the possible orders of A and B? What are these orders if AB and BA both have the same order?

2

Solution. If A has order $r \times s$ then B must have order $s \times r$ so that AB has order $r \times r$ and BA has order $s \times s$. Consequently if AB and BA have the same order $r = s$ and A and B are square matrices of the same order. $\square$

Problem 1.5 Calculate the products AB and BA where $A = \begin{bmatrix} 1 & 3 \\ 2 & 1 \end{bmatrix}$,

$B = \begin{bmatrix} 4 & 0 \\ 2 & 1 \end{bmatrix}$.

Solution. We find $AB = \begin{bmatrix} 10 & 3 \\ 10 & 1 \end{bmatrix}$, $BA = \begin{bmatrix} 4 & 12 \\ 4 & 7 \end{bmatrix}$ so that $AB \neq BA$.

$\square$

Problem 1.6 Find non-zero square matrices B, C such that $AB = 0 = CA$ where $A = \begin{bmatrix} 1 & -1 \\ 2 & -2 \end{bmatrix}$.

Solution. The elements of $B = [b_{ij}]$ have to satisfy the equations
$$b_{11} - b_{21} = 0, \quad 2b_{11} - 2b_{21} = 0, \quad b_{12} - b_{22} = 0, \quad 2b_{12} - 2b_{22} = 0.$$
These equations have many solutions and similarly there are many possibilities for the elements of C. Particular choices are $B = \begin{bmatrix} 1 & 1 \\ 1 & 1 \end{bmatrix}$,

$C = \begin{bmatrix} 2 & -1 \\ 2 & -1 \end{bmatrix}$. The matrices A, B, C are examples of divisors of zero.

$\square$

Problem 1.7 The equations $x_1 + x_2 + x_3 = 1$, $2x_1 + x_2 + 2x_3 = 0$, $3x_1 + 2x_2 + 4x_3 = 1$ are simultaneous equations to determine the three unknowns x_1, x_2, x_3. Show that they can be written as a single matrix equation.

Solution. The equations can be written in matrix form as

$$\begin{bmatrix} 1 & 1 & 1 \\ 2 & 1 & 2 \\ 3 & 2 & 4 \end{bmatrix} \begin{bmatrix} x_1 \\ x_2 \\ x_3 \end{bmatrix} = \begin{bmatrix} 1 \\ 0 \\ 1 \end{bmatrix}.$$

It is clear that any set of linear equations can be written in the same way as a single matrix equation $Ax = h$ where x is the column vector formed from the unknowns. $\square$

Problems 1.5 and 1.6 show that there are considerable differences between the algebra of real or complex numbers and that of matrices. But there are also some important similarities.

3

Problem 1.8 Show that the distributive laws are satisfied, that is $A(B+C) = AB+AC$, $(B+C)A = BA+CA$ where, in each case, A, B, C are any matrices for which the operations are defined.

Solution. To prove the first law suppose that $A = [a_{ij}]$ has order $r \times s$ and that $B = [b_{ij}]$, $C = [c_{ij}]$ both have order $s \times t$. From the definition of matrix multiplication $AB = [h_{ij}]$, $AC = [k_{ij}]$ where

$$h_{ij} = \sum_{d=1}^{s} a_{id}b_{dj}, \qquad k_{ij} = \sum_{d=1}^{s} a_{id}c_{dj}.$$

Hence $AB+AC = [h_{ij}+k_{ij}] = [\sum_{d=1}^{s} a_{id}(b_{dj}+c_{dj})] = A(B+C)$.

The second law can be proved in a similar way. $\square$

Problem 1.9 Show that

$$AO = OA = O; \quad A(-B) = -(AB) = (-A)B;$$
$$A(B-C) = AB-AC, \quad (B-C)A = BA-CA.$$

Solution. The first two sets of relations are obvious from the definition of the multiplication of matrices. The third then follows from the distributive law. For $A(B-C) = A(B+(-C)) = AB+A(-C) = AB-AC$ and similar steps hold for the last relation. $\square$

The multiplication of matrices also satisfies the associative law, that is $A(BC) = (AB)C$ whenever the multiplications are defined.

Problem 1.10 Variables (x_1, x_2), (y_1, y_2), (z_1, z_2) are related by $y_1 = 2x_1 + x_2$, $y_2 = x_1 + 2x_2$; $z_1 = y_1 - y_2$, $z_2 = y_1 + y_2$. Find the relation between the variables (x_1, x_2) and (z_1, z_2).

Solution. The given relations can be written in matrix form as $y = Ax$, $z = By$ where

$$A = \begin{bmatrix} 2 & 1 \\ 1 & 2 \end{bmatrix}, \quad B = \begin{bmatrix} 1 & -1 \\ 1 & 1 \end{bmatrix}, \quad x = \begin{bmatrix} x_1 \\ x_2 \end{bmatrix}, \quad y = \begin{bmatrix} y_1 \\ y_2 \end{bmatrix}, \quad z = \begin{bmatrix} z_1 \\ z_2 \end{bmatrix}.$$

Using the associative law we obtain $z = By = B(Ax) = (BA)x$ and a calculation of the matrix product BA shows that

$$z_1 = x_1 - x_2, \qquad z_2 = 3x_1 + 3x_2.$$

It is clear that linear transformations in any number of variables can be handled in the same way. $\square$

Problem 1.2 shows that the associative law is important in solving equations. But in dealing with equations involving multiplication we first need the matrices corresponding to the zero and negative. These

4

matrices are called unit and inverse matrices. A *unit matrix* is a square matrix with 1's along the leading diagonal and zeros elsewhere. Thus a unit matrix is $[\delta_{rs}]$ where δ_{rs} is a symbol called the *Kronecker delta*, defined by $\delta_{rs} = 0$ $(r \neq s)$, $\delta_{rr} = 1$. We denote a unit matrix by I independently of its order. If A is any matrix then $IA = A = AI$ where the two symbols I may denote unit matrices of different orders.

A matrix B is said to be inverse to a square matrix A if $AB = BA = I$. B is necessarily of the same order as A. $\qquad\qquad\qquad\qquad\qquad$ □

Problem 1.11 Show that a square matrix A has at most one inverse.

Solution. Suppose that B, C are both inverses of A. Then $B = IB = (CA)B = C(AB) = CI = C$.

Problem 1.12 A, B are square matrices with inverses A^{-1}, B^{-1} respectively. Prove that $(A^{-1})^{-1} = A, (AB)^{-1} = B^{-1}A^{-1}$.

Solution. The first relation follows at once from $AA^{-1} = I = A^{-1}A$. To prove the second we have to show that $(AB)(B^{-1}A^{-1}) = I = (B^{-1}A^{-1})(AB)$. Using the associative law we have that $(AB)(B^{-1}A^{-1}) = A(B(B^{-1}A^{-1})) = A((BB^{-1})A^{-1}) = AA^{-1} = I$ and the second equality can be proved in a similar way. $\qquad\qquad\qquad\qquad\qquad$ □

Problem 1.13 Show that if A has an inverse then the equation $AX = H$ has the unique solution $X = A^{-1}H$.

Solution. $A^{-1}H$ is a solution because $A(A^{-1}H) = (AA^{-1})H = IH = H$. It is the only solution because if $AX = H$ then $X = IX = (A^{-1}A)X = A^{-1}(AX) = A^{-1}H$. $\qquad\qquad\qquad\qquad\qquad$ □

Problem 1.14 Show that the matrix

$$A = \begin{bmatrix} 1 & 1 & 1 \\ 2 & 1 & 2 \\ 3 & 2 & 4 \end{bmatrix} \text{ has inverse } A^{-1} = \begin{bmatrix} 0 & 2 & -1 \\ 2 & -1 & 0 \\ -1 & -1 & 1 \end{bmatrix}.$$

Solve the simultaneous equations

$$x_1 + x_2 + x_3 = 1, \qquad 2x_1 + x_2 + 2x_3 = 0, \qquad 3x_1 + 2x_2 + 4x_3 = 1.$$

Solution. It is easy to verify that the product of the matrices (in either order) is a unit matrix. The equations can be written in the form $Ax = h$ and therefore have the unique solution

$$x = A^{-1}h = \begin{bmatrix} 0 & 2 & -1 \\ 2 & -1 & 0 \\ -1 & -1 & 1 \end{bmatrix} \begin{bmatrix} 1 \\ 0 \\ 1 \end{bmatrix} = \begin{bmatrix} -1 \\ 2 \\ 0 \end{bmatrix}.$$

$\qquad\qquad\qquad\qquad\qquad$ □

In the algebra of real or complex numbers the only element which does not have an inverse is the zero. This is not so in matrix algebra.

Problem 1.15 Use Problem 1.13 to show that the matrix $A = \begin{bmatrix} 1 & -1 \\ 2 & -2 \end{bmatrix}$ does not have an inverse.

Solution. The equation $Ax = 0$, where x is a column vector has other solutions than the zero vector and so A cannot have an inverse.

□

Problem 1.16 Find a condition for a 2×2 matrix to have an inverse.

Solution. Let $A = [a_{ij}]$ be a 2×2 matrix. In order to find an inverse matrix we have to find a 2×2 matrix $B = [b_{ij}]$ such that $AB = I$, and this condition leads to

$$a_{11}b_{11}+a_{12}b_{12} = 1 \qquad a_{11}b_{12}+a_{12}b_{22} = 0$$
$$a_{21}b_{11}+a_{22}b_{21} = 0 \qquad a_{21}b_{12}+a_{22}b_{22} = 1$$

We try to solve these equations for the unknowns b_{ij}. Starting with the first set of two equations we multiply the first equation by a_{22}, the second by a_{12} and subtract. This gives $(a_{11}a_{22}-a_{12}a_{21})b_{11} = a_{22}$. Repeating the process but using a_{21} instead of a_{22}, a_{11} instead of a_{12}, we obtain $(a_{11}a_{22}-a_{12}a_{21})b_{21} = -a_{21}$. The same operations on the second set of equations give $(a_{11}a_{22}-a_{12}a_{21})b_{12} = -a_{12}$, $(a_{11}a_{22}-a_{12}a_{21})b_{22} = a_{11}$. It follows that if the expression $a_{11}a_{22}-a_{12}a_{21}$ is not zero then there is a unique matrix B such that $AB = I$. It is easy to check that BA also is equal to I and so A has an inverse.

The number $a_{11}a_{22}-a_{12}a_{21}$ is called the determinant of the 2×2 matrix A and is denoted by det A or $|A|$. If $|A| \neq 0$ then A has an inverse. In Chapter 2 we give a definition of the determinant of a square matrix of any order. □

1.4 Scalar Multiplication of a Matrix Given a number λ and a matrix $A = [a_{ij}]$ we define a matrix λA by $\lambda A = [\lambda a_{ij}]$. This operation is the scalar multiplication of A by λ. As an example of its use we note that the formulae in Problem 1.16 can be expressed by

$$A^{-1} = \frac{1}{|A|} \begin{bmatrix} a_{22} & -a_{12} \\ -a_{21} & a_{11} \end{bmatrix}.$$

Scalar multiplication satisfies certain simple laws which relate it to the addition and multiplication of matrices. We list them as follows:

$$\lambda(A+B) = \lambda A+\lambda B, \qquad (\lambda+\mu)A = \lambda A+\mu A.$$
$$\lambda(\mu A) = (\lambda\mu)A, \qquad 1A = A, \qquad \lambda(AB) = (\lambda A)B = A(\lambda B).$$

Problem 1.17 Prove that $(\lambda A)^{-1} = \lambda^{-1}A^{-1}$ where $\lambda \neq 0$ and A is a square matrix with an inverse.

Solution. We have to show that $(\lambda A)(\lambda^{-1}A^{-1}) = I = (\lambda^{-1}A^{-1})(\lambda A)$. We find $(\lambda A)(\lambda^{-1}A^{-1}) = \lambda(A(\lambda^{-1}A^{-1})) = \lambda(\lambda^{-1}(AA^{-1})) = 1I = I$ and the other equality can be proved in a similar way.

Problem 1.18 Prove that $x[\lambda] = \lambda x$, $[\lambda]y = \lambda y$ where x is a column vector, y is a row vector and $[\lambda]$ is the 1×1 matrix with element λ.

Solution. $x[\lambda] = \begin{bmatrix} x_1 \\ \vdots \\ x_n \end{bmatrix}[\lambda] = \begin{bmatrix} \lambda x_1 \\ \vdots \\ \lambda x_n \end{bmatrix} = \lambda x,$

$$[\lambda]y = [\lambda][y_1 \ldots y_n] = [\lambda y_1 \ldots \lambda y_n] = \lambda y. \qquad \square$$

1.5 Partitioned Matrices Suppose that matrices A and B are partitioned into submatrices. Then the product AB can be obtained by applying the rule for matrix multiplication to the submatrices. Of course, this statement is subject to the condition that the various multiplications are defined.

Problem 1.19 Use an appropriate partitioning of A to calculate A^2 where

$$A = \begin{bmatrix} 1 & 0 & 1 & 2 \\ 0 & 1 & 2 & 4 \\ 0 & 0 & 2 & 1 \\ 0 & 0 & 1 & 2 \end{bmatrix}.$$

Solution. $A = \begin{bmatrix} I & X \\ O & Y \end{bmatrix}$ where $X = \begin{bmatrix} 1 & 2 \\ 2 & 4 \end{bmatrix}$ and $Y = \begin{bmatrix} 2 & 1 \\ 1 & 2 \end{bmatrix}$.

Consequently $A^2 = \begin{bmatrix} I & X + XY \\ O & Y^2 \end{bmatrix}$ and we substitute for X and Y to

obtain

$$A^2 = \begin{bmatrix} 1 & 0 & 5 & 7 \\ 0 & 1 & 10 & 14 \\ 0 & 0 & 5 & 4 \\ 0 & 0 & 4 & 5 \end{bmatrix}. \qquad \square$$

Problem 1.20 A square matrix is partitioned as $A = \begin{bmatrix} F & G \\ O & H \end{bmatrix}$

where F and H have inverses. Show that A has an inverse and express it in terms of F, G and H.

Solution. We look for a matrix B partitioned in exactly the same way as A and such that $AB = I$. We put

$$AB = \begin{bmatrix} F & G \\ O & H \end{bmatrix}\begin{bmatrix} W & X \\ Y & Z \end{bmatrix} = I = \begin{bmatrix} I & O \\ O & I \end{bmatrix}$$

and this leads to the matrix equations

(1) $FW + GY = I$ (2) $HY = O$ (3) $FX + GZ = O$ (4) $HZ = I$

for the unknowns W, X, Y, Z. As H has an inverse (2) shows that $Y = O$ and therefore (1) gives $W = F^{-1}$. The equation (4) shows that $Z = H^{-1}$ and consequently (3) becomes $FX + GH^{-1} = O$. We multiply this equation on the left by F^{-1} to obtain $X = -F^{-1}GH^{-1}$. It follows that the matrix $B = \begin{bmatrix} F^{-1} & -F^{-1}GH^{-1} \\ O & H^{-1} \end{bmatrix}$ satisfies $AB = I$ and it is easy to check that also $BA = I$. Thus B is the inverse of A.   □

Problem 1.21   Use Problem 1.20 to find the inverse of

$$A = \begin{bmatrix} 3 & 1 & -3 & -1 \\ 1 & 1 & 0 & -2 \\ 0 & 0 & 3 & 2 \\ 0 & 0 & -1 & -1 \end{bmatrix}.$$

Solution. The inverse of the given matrix is $\begin{bmatrix} F^{-1} & -F^{-1}GH^{-1} \\ O & H^{-1} \end{bmatrix}$

where $F = \begin{bmatrix} 3 & 1 \\ 1 & 1 \end{bmatrix}$, $G = \begin{bmatrix} -3 & -1 \\ 0 & -2 \end{bmatrix}$, $H = \begin{bmatrix} 3 & 2 \\ -1 & -1 \end{bmatrix}$. Using the

formula in 1.4 for the inverse of a 2×2 matrix we find that

$$A^{-1} = \begin{bmatrix} \frac{1}{2} & -\frac{1}{2} & 2 & \frac{9}{2} \\ -\frac{1}{2} & \frac{3}{2} & -4 & -\frac{21}{2} \\ 0 & 0 & 1 & 2 \\ 0 & 0 & -1 & -3 \end{bmatrix}.$$

   □

A diagonal matrix is a square matrix $\Lambda = [\lambda_{ij}]$ such that $\lambda_{ij} = 0$ if $i \neq j$. The elements $\lambda_i = \lambda_{ii}$ are the diagonal elements and we often write $\Lambda = \text{diag}\{\lambda_1, \ldots, \lambda_n\}$.

Problem 1.22 T is a matrix partitioned into its column vectors

$v_1, \ldots, v_n$. What are the column vectors of the matrices AT and $T\Lambda$ where $\Lambda = \text{diag}\{\lambda_1, \ldots, \lambda_n\}$?

Solution. In the first multiplication we regard A as partitioned into the single submatrix A and T as partitioned into its column vectors. Because $AT = A[v_1 \ldots v_n] = [Av_1 \ldots Av_n]$ it follows that the column vectors of AT are $Av_1, \ldots, Av_n$.

In the second multiplication we regard T as partitioned into its column vectors and Λ as partitioned into its single elements considered as 1×1 submatrices. Then

$$T\Lambda = [v_1[\lambda_1] \ldots v_n[\lambda_n]] = [\lambda_1 v_1 \ldots \lambda_n v_n]$$

where the last step follows from Problem 1.18. Consequently the column vectors of $T\Lambda$ are $\lambda_1 v_1, \ldots, \lambda_n v_n$.

1.6 The Transposition of Matrices The transpose A' of a matrix A is defined by $A' = [a'_{ij}]$ where $a'_{ij} = a_{ji}$. Thus the rows of A become the columns of A'. If A is of order $m \times n$ then A' is of order $n \times m$.

Problem 1.23 u, v are column vectors of the same order. Calculate the matrices $u'v, uv'$.

Solution. In order to save space we will often express a column vector as the transpose of a row vector. Thus in this case we write $u = [u_1 \ldots u_n]'$, $v = [v_1 \ldots v_n]'$. Then $u'v$ is the 1×1 matrix $[u_1 v_1 + \ldots + u_n v_n]$ and uv' is the $n \times n$ matrix $[u_i v_j]$. $\qquad \square$

Problem 1.24 Prove that $(A')' = A$, $(A+B)' = A' + B'$, $(AB)' = B'A'$. Show that if A has an inverse then the inverse of A' is $(A^{-1})'$.

Solution. The first two equalities are obvious. To prove the third we suppose that $A = [a_{ij}]$ is of order $r \times s$ and that $B = [b_{ij}]$ is of order $s \times t$ so that AB is defined. We write $A' = [a'_{ij}]$ and $B' = [b'_{ij}]$ where $a'_{ij} = a_{ji}$ and $b'_{ij} = b_{ji}$. It follows that

$$B'A' = \left[\sum_{k=1}^{s} b'_{ik} a'_{kj}\right] = \left[\sum_{k=1}^{s} a_{jk} b_{ki}\right] = (AB)'.$$

Finally we use this multiplication rule to transpose the relations $AA^{-1} = I = A^{-1}A$. We obtain $(A^{-1})'(A^{-1})'A' = I = A'(A^{-1})'$ and these show that $(A')^{-1} = (A^{-1})'$. $\qquad \square$

A square matrix A is *symmetric* if $A' = A$ or, in terms of its elements, if $a_{ji} = a_{ij}$. A is *skew-symmetric* if $A' = -A$ that is if $a_{ji} = -a_{ij}$. If A

9

is skew-symmetric then, in particular, $a_{ii} = -a_{ii}$ so that $a_{ii} = 0$. Thus the diagonal elements of a skew-symmetric matrix are all zero.

Problem 1.25 Prove that any square matrix M can be expressed uniquely as $M = A + B$ where A is symmetric and B is skew-symmetric.

Solution. We can certainly express M in this form because $M = \frac{1}{2}(M + M') + \frac{1}{2}(M - M')$ and the matrices $\frac{1}{2}(M + M')$ and $\frac{1}{2}(M - M')$ are symmetric and skew-symmetric respectively. On the other hand if M is so expressed as $M = A + B$ then $M' = A' + B' = A - B$ and these two equations determine A and B uniquely in terms of M and M'. ∎

Problem 1.26 Prove that if A is symmetric or skew-symmetric then so is the matrix $T'AT$. If x is a column vector and B is skew-symmetric deduce that $x'Bx = 0$.

Solution. Let A be of order $n \times n$ so that T must be of order $n \times r$. Then T' is of order $r \times n$ and the matrix $T'AT$ is defined. By a simple extension of the multiplication rule in Problem 1.24, $(T'AT)' = T'A'(T')' = T'A'T$. Consequently $(T'AT)' = \pm T'AT$ according as $A' = \pm A$. In particular, if T is a column vector x and A is a skew-symmetric matrix B then $x'Bx$ is a skew-symmetric matrix of order 1×1. But any such matrix is zero. ∎

A *real quadratic form* in n real variables $x_1, \ldots, x_n$ is a function $\Sigma m_{ij} x_i x_j (i, j = 1, \ldots, n)$, where the m_{ij} are real numbers. It can be written very simply in matrix form as the element in the 1×1 matrix $x'Mx$ where $M = [m_{ij}]$ and $x = [x_1 \ldots x_n]'$. It follows from Problems 1.25 and 1.26 that $x'Mx = x'Ax$ where A is a symmetric matrix. A is called the matrix of the quadratic form and is uniquely determined by it. If new variables $y_1, \ldots, y_n$ are defined in terms of $x_1, \ldots, x_n$ by a linear relation $x = Ty$ then the quadratic form is expressed in terms of the new variables as $(Ty)'A(Ty) = y'T'ATy$. This is a quadratic form in the variables $y_1, \ldots, y_n$ and Problem 1.26 shows that the corresponding matrix is $T'AT$.

Problem 1.27 The equation $5x_1^2 - 6x_1x_2 + 5x_2^2 = 8$ in rectangular cartesian coordinates (x_1, x_2) represents a central conic. Let (y_1, y_2) denote a second system of coordinates obtained by a rotation of the coordinate axes. Show that it is possible to choose the angle of rotation so that the equation of the conic is $\lambda_1 y_1^2 + \lambda_2 y_2^2 = 1$, and find values for λ_1, λ_2.

Solution. Suppose that the coordinate axes are rotated through an

10

angle α. Then with $x = [x_1\, x_2]'$, $y = [y_1\, y_2]'$ we have $x = Ty$ where
$T = \begin{bmatrix} \cos\alpha & -\sin\alpha \\ \sin\alpha & \cos\alpha \end{bmatrix}$. Pur $A = \begin{bmatrix} 5 & -3 \\ -3 & 5 \end{bmatrix}$ so that the equation of
the conic in matrix notation is $x'Ax = 8$ where we have omitted the
matrix brackets on the right-hand side. To obtain the equation of the
conic in the new coordinates we have to substitute $x = Ty$. We find
$y'T'ATy = 8$. A calculation gives

$$T'AT = \begin{bmatrix} 5-3\sin 2\alpha & -3\cos 2\alpha \\ -3\cos 2\alpha & 5+3\sin 2\alpha \end{bmatrix}$$

and this is a diagonal matrix if $\alpha = \pi/4$. With this choice the equation
of the conic is $2y_1^2 + 8y_2^2 = 8$ or $\frac{1}{4}y_1^2 + y_2^2 = 1$. □

Problem 1.28 A is an $n \times n$ matrix with an inverse, x, y are column
vectors of order $n \times 1$ and k is a scalar. Calculate the products
$(A+xy')A^{-1}(I-kxy'A^{-1})$ and $A^{-1}(I-kxy'A^{-1})(A+xy')$. If α is the
element of the matrix $y'A^{-1}x$ and $1+\alpha \neq 0$ deduce that
$$(A+xy')^{-1} = A^{-1}(I-(1+\alpha)^{-1}xy'A^{-1}).$$

Solution. We expand the brackets in the first product to obtain
$$I - kxy'A^{-1} + xy'A^{-1} - kxy'A^{-1}xy'A^{-1}.$$
Because $y'A^{-1}x = [\alpha]$, Problem 1.18 shows that the last term is
$-k\alpha xy'A^{-1}$ and therefore the product is equal to $I+(1-k(1+\alpha))xy'A^{-1}$.
The second product reduces in a similar way to $I+(1-k(1+\alpha))A^{-1}xy'$.
If $k = (1+\alpha)^{-1}$ these products are both equal to I and consequently
$$(A+xy')^{-1} = A^{-1}(I-(1+\alpha)^{-1}xy'\,A^{-1}).$$ □

Problem 1.29 Use Problem 1.28 to calculate the inverse of the
$n \times n$ matrix $B = [b_{ij}]$ where $b_{ij} = 1$ $(i \neq j)$, $b_{ii} = 2$.
Solution. $B = I+xx'$ where $x = [1 \ldots 1]'$. Therefore $B^{-1} = I(I-(1+\alpha)^{-1}xx')$ where α is the element of the matrix $x'Ix = x'x$.
Consequently $\alpha = n$ and the elements β_{ij} of the matrix B^{-1} are given
by $\beta_{ij} = -(1+n)^{-1}$ $(i \neq j)$, $\beta_{ii} = n(1+n)^{-1}$. □

1.7 Complex Matrices The *complex conjugate* $\bar{A}$ of a matrix
$A = [a_{ij}]$ is defined by $\bar{A} = [\bar{a}_{ij}]$ where $\bar{a}_{ij}$ is the complex conjugate
of a_{ij}. It is clear that the complex conjugate of $\bar{A}$ is A. The operation
fits in simply with the others we have introduced. Thus $\overline{A+B} = \bar{A}+\bar{B}$, $\overline{AB} = \bar{A}\bar{B}$, $\overline{\lambda A} = \bar{\lambda}\bar{A}$ and $\overline{(A')} = (\bar{A})'$.

Problem 1.30 What are $\bar{B}, \bar{B}', \bar{C}, \bar{C}'$ if $B = \begin{bmatrix} 2 & 1+i \\ 1-i & 3 \end{bmatrix}$,

$C = \begin{bmatrix} 2i & -1+i \\ 1+i & 3i \end{bmatrix}$.

Solution. The matrices are, respectively,

$$\begin{bmatrix} 2 & 1-i \\ 1+i & 3 \end{bmatrix}, \begin{bmatrix} 2 & 1+i \\ 1-i & 3 \end{bmatrix}, \begin{bmatrix} -2i & -1-i \\ 1-i & -3i \end{bmatrix}, \begin{bmatrix} -2i & 1-i \\ -1-i & -3i \end{bmatrix}. \quad \square$$

There is a generalization of the ideas of symmetric and skew-symmetric real matrices to the complex case. A square matrix A is *hermitian* if $\bar{A}' = A$ or, in terms of its elements, if $\bar{a}_{ji} = a_{ij}$. A is *skew-hermitian* if $\bar{A}' = -A$ that is if $\bar{a}_{ji} = -a_{ij}$. For example, in Problem 1.30 B is hermitian and C is skew-hermitian. If A is hermitian then, in particular, $\bar{a}_{ii} = a_{ii}$ and so the diagonal elements are all real. Similarly if A is skew-hermitian then the diagonal elements are purely imaginary.

Problem 1.31 Prove that if A is hermitian or skew-hermitian then so is $\bar{T}'AT$. Deduce that if z is a column vector then $\bar{z}'Az$ is real if A is hermitian and is purely imaginary if A is skew-hermitian.

Solution. $(\overline{\bar{T}'AT})' = (T'\bar{A}\bar{T})' = \bar{T}'\bar{A}'T$ and consequently $(\overline{\bar{T}'AT})' = \pm\bar{T}'AT$ according as $\bar{A}' = \pm A$. The last part of the problem follows from the remark that $\bar{z}'Az$ is a 1×1 matrix and such a matrix is hermitian or skew-hermitian according as its element is real or purely imaginary. $\quad \square$

EXERCISES

1. (i) Calculate $A^2 - B^2, (A-B)(A+B)$ where $A = \begin{bmatrix} 1 & 3 \\ 2 & 1 \end{bmatrix}, B = \begin{bmatrix} 4 & 0 \\ 2 & 1 \end{bmatrix}$.

   (ii) Test $A(BC) = (AB)C$ with A, B as in (i) and $C = \begin{bmatrix} 1 & 1 \\ 0 & 1 \end{bmatrix}$.

2. Simplify $(A+B-I)(A-B+I)+(A+2B)(B-A)$. Test by calculating the expression and your simplification with A, B as in question 1.

3. Matrices A, B are said to commute if $AB = BA$. Find all the matrices which commute with diag$\{1, 2, 3\}$.

4. $A = [a_{ij}]$ is a real 2×2 matrix and O is the origin of rectangular cartesian coordinates in the euclidean plane. Let P, Q denote the

points of coordinates (a_{11}, a_{21}), (a_{12}, a_{22}) respectively. Prove that the area of the parallelogram with sides OP, OQ is equal to the absolute value of $|A|$. Deduce that $|A|^2 \leqslant (a_{11}^2 + a_{21}^2)(a_{12}^2 + a_{22}^2)$.

5. Find the inverse of the partitioned matrix $\begin{bmatrix} I & B \\ O & A \end{bmatrix}$ where

$$A = \begin{bmatrix} 2 & -4 \\ -1 & 3 \end{bmatrix}, \qquad B = \begin{bmatrix} 3 & -1 \\ 1 & -5 \\ -2 & 6 \end{bmatrix}.$$

6. (i) If A, B are skew-symmetric matrices show that $AB - BA$ is also skew-symmetric.

(ii) If A is any complex matrix show that $A\bar{A}'$ and $\bar{A}'A$ are hermitian. If A is hermitian show that iA is skew-hermitian.

Chapter 2

The Determinant of a Square Matrix

2.1 Permutations The determinant of a 2×2 matrix has been defined in Chapter I. The generalization of the definition to a square matrix of arbitrary order requires some knowledge of permutations.

We regard a *permutation* of the integers $1, 2, \ldots, n$ as a re-arrangement of these integers. For example 43152 is a permutation of the integers $1, 2, 3, 4, 5$. We express this by $12345 \rightarrow 43152$. Including the identity permutation $12 \ldots n$ there are n! permutations of the integers $1, 2, \ldots, n$.

A permutation such as $12345 \rightarrow 14325$ in which just two integers are interchanged is called an *interchange*. Any permutation can be obtained by a succession of interchanges. A permutation is said to be an *even* or an *odd permutation* of the integers $1, 2, \ldots, n$ according as it can be obtained by an even or an odd number of interchanges. Of course for the definition to make sense it has to be proved that the number of interchanges required to obtain a given permutation is either always even or always odd.

Problem 2.1 Obtain the permutation $12345 \rightarrow 43152$ by a succession of interchanges in two ways. Verify that both ways involve an even number of interchanges.

Solution. (i) $12345 \rightarrow 42315 \rightarrow 43215 \rightarrow 43125 \rightarrow 43152$.
(ii) $12345 \rightarrow 13245 \rightarrow 13425 \rightarrow 13452 \rightarrow 31452 \rightarrow 34152 \rightarrow 43152$.
The first way involves 4 interchanges and the second 6. □

Problem 2.2 Obtain all the permutations of (i) 1,2 (ii) 1,2,3. In each case separate the permutations into odd and even ones.

Solution. (i) $2! = 2$ permutations, 12 and 21. 12 is even and 21 odd.
(ii) $3! = 6$ permutations. Consider the permutation 231. It can be obtained by 2 interchanges $123 \rightarrow 213 \rightarrow 231$ and is therefore an even permutation. We find in this way that 123, 231, 312 are even and 132, 213, 321 are odd. □

2.2 The Definition of a Determinant Let $A = [a_{ij}]$ be an $n \times n$ matrix. The *determinant* $|A|$ of A is defined by

$$|A| = \sum \pm a_{1\alpha} a_{2\beta} \ldots a_{n\kappa} \qquad (2.1)$$

where the sum is over all the permutations $\alpha\beta \ldots \kappa$ of $1, 2, \ldots, n$, the sign being $\pm$ according as the permutation is even or odd.

14

Problem 2.3 Write out the terms in the sum in definition (2.1) for matrices of orders 2×2 and 3×3.

Solution. We find from Problem 2.2 that

$$\begin{vmatrix} a_{11} & a_{12} \\ a_{21} & a_{22} \end{vmatrix} = a_{11}\,a_{22} - a_{12}\,a_{21}\,,$$

$$\begin{vmatrix} a_{11} & a_{12} & a_{13} \\ a_{21} & a_{22} & a_{23} \\ a_{31} & a_{32} & a_{33} \end{vmatrix} = \begin{aligned} &a_{11}\,a_{22}\,a_{33} + a_{12}\,a_{23}\,a_{31} + a_{13}\,a_{21}\,a_{32} \\ &- a_{11}\,a_{13}\,a_{32} - a_{12}\,a_{21}\,a_{33} - a_{13}\,a_{22}\,a_{31}\,. \end{aligned}$$

We see that definition (2.1) agrees with the previous definition for 2×2 matrices given in Problem 1.16.

Problem 2.4 Prove that $|A'| = |A|$.

Solution. We write $A = [a_{ij}]$ and $A' = [a'_{ij}]$ where $a'_{ij} = a_{ji}$. From the definition (2.1)

$$|A'| = \sum \pm a'_{1\alpha} a'_{2\beta} \ldots a'_{n\kappa} = \sum \pm a_{\alpha 1}\, a_{\beta 2} \ldots a_{\kappa n}$$

where the sum is over all permutations $\alpha\beta \ldots \kappa$ of $1, 2, \ldots, n$ the sign being $\pm$ according as the permutation is even or odd. We can rearrange the product $a_{\alpha 1}\, a_{\beta 2} \ldots a_{\kappa n}$ as $a_{1\alpha'}\, a_{2\beta'} \ldots a_{n\kappa'}$ where $\alpha'\beta' \ldots \kappa'$ is a permutation of $1, 2, \ldots, n$ determined uniquely by $\alpha\beta \ldots \kappa$. Indeed if we re-arrange the product by a succession of interchanges of the elements these interchanges will give both of the permutations $\alpha\beta \ldots \kappa \to 12 \ldots n$ and $12 \ldots n \to \alpha'\beta' \ldots \kappa'$. It follows that the permutations $\alpha\beta \ldots \kappa$ and $\alpha'\beta' \ldots \kappa'$ are both even or both odd. Consequently

$$|A'| = \sum \pm a_{1\alpha'}\, a_{2\beta'} \ldots a_{n\kappa'}$$

where the sum is over all permutations $\alpha'\beta' \ldots \kappa'$ of $1, 2, \ldots n$ the sign being $\pm$ according as the permutation is even or odd. Therefore $|A'| = |A|$. ☐

Problem 2.5 Prove that the determinant of a lower or upper triangular matrix is equal to the product of its diagonal elements.

Solution. We suppose that the square matrix $A = [a_{ij}]$ is *lower triangular* so that $a_{ij} = 0$ for $j > i$. Then in the definition (2.1) the only non-zero term in the sum is $\pm a_{11}\, a_{22} \ldots a_{nn}$. The corresponding permutation is the identity and so the sign is $+$. Therefore $|A| = a_{11}\, a_{22} \ldots a_{nn}$.

Suppose now that the square matrix $B = [b_{ij}]$ is *upper triangular* so that $b_{ij} = 0$ for $i > j$. Then B' is lower triangular and has the same diagonal terms as B. We have seen that $|B'| = b_{11}\, b_{22} \ldots b_{nn}$, and Problem 2.4 shows that $|B| = |B'|$. ☐

2.3 Properties of a Determinant It is obvious that the direct use of the definition (2.1) is not a reasonable method for calculating the determinant of a matrix. The following properties of a determinant lead to efficient methods. The properties are stated for rows only but are also true for columns.

D1. Interchanging any two rows of a matrix changes the sign of its determinant.

D2. Multiplying each element in a row of a matrix by λ multiplies its determinant by λ.

D3. If a row of a matrix is expressed as the sum of two row vectors then its determinant can be expressed as the sum of two corresponding determinants. For example

$$\begin{vmatrix} a_1 & b_1 & c_1 \\ a_2+\alpha & b_2+\beta & c_2+\gamma \\ a_3 & b_3 & c_3 \end{vmatrix} = \begin{vmatrix} a_1 & b_1 & c_1 \\ a_2 & b_2 & c_2 \\ a_3 & b_3 & c_3 \end{vmatrix} + \begin{vmatrix} a_1 & b_1 & c_1 \\ \alpha & \beta & \gamma \\ a_3 & b_3 & c_3 \end{vmatrix}.$$

The properties D1, D2, D3 are easy deductions from the definition (2.1). The same properties for columns follow almost at once from Problem 2.4.

Problem 2.6 Prove that if a square matrix has two equal rows (or columns) then its determinant is zero.

Solution. Suppose that A has two equal rows. Interchanging the two rows does not alter the matrix but property D1 shows that the determinant changes sign. Consequently $|A| = -|A|$ so that $|A| = 0$. A similar proof works for columns. □

Problem 2.7 A matrix B is obtained from a square matrix A by adding to a row of A a multiple of another row of A. Prove that $|B| = |A|$.

Solution. Partition A into its row vectors so that

$$A = \begin{bmatrix} \vdots \\ u \\ \vdots \\ v \\ \vdots \end{bmatrix}, \qquad B = \begin{bmatrix} \vdots \\ u+\lambda v \\ \vdots \\ v \\ \vdots \end{bmatrix}.$$

It follows from properties D3 and D2 that $|B| = |A| + \lambda|C|$ where C is a matrix with two rows equal to v. Problem 2.6 shows that $|C| = 0$. An analogous result is true for columns. □

16

Problem 2.8 Calculate the determinants of the matrices:

(i) $A = \begin{bmatrix} 2 & -2 & 4 & -4 \\ 3 & -2 & 6 & 5 \\ 0 & 1 & 1 & -3 \\ -2 & -1 & 5 & 6 \end{bmatrix}$ (ii) $B = \begin{bmatrix} 0 & 1 & 2 \\ 3 & -4 & 8 \\ 1 & 3 & 5 \end{bmatrix}$.

Solution. (i) We work to produce an upper triangular matrix and then apply Problem 2.5. We use property D2 to take a factor 2 from the first row and then carry out the operations (row 2)-3(row 1) and (row 4)$+2$(row 1). Problem 2.7 shows that these operations do not affect the determinant of a matrix and so

$$|A| = 2 \begin{vmatrix} 1 & -1 & 2 & -2 \\ 3 & -2 & 6 & 5 \\ 0 & 1 & 1 & -3 \\ -2 & -1 & 5 & 6 \end{vmatrix} = 2 \begin{vmatrix} 1 & -1 & 2 & -2 \\ 0 & 1 & 0 & 11 \\ 0 & 1 & 1 & -3 \\ 0 & -3 & 9 & 2 \end{vmatrix}$$

Working with the new matrix we carry out the operations (row 3)$-$(row 2) and (row 4)$+3$(row 2) which lead to

$$|A| = 2 \begin{vmatrix} 1 & -1 & 2 & -2 \\ 0 & 1 & 0 & 11 \\ 0 & 0 & 1 & -14 \\ 0 & 0 & 9 & 35 \end{vmatrix}$$

Finally the operation (row 4)-9(row 3) shows that

$$|A| = 2 \begin{vmatrix} 1 & -1 & 2 & -2 \\ 0 & 1 & 0 & 11 \\ 0 & 0 & 1 & -14 \\ 0 & 0 & 0 & 161 \end{vmatrix} = 322.$$

(ii) In this case we interchange the first two rows and take a factor 3 from the new first row. Then we proceed as in (i) to obtain

$$|B| = -3 \begin{vmatrix} 1 & -\frac{4}{3} & \frac{8}{3} \\ 0 & 1 & 2 \\ 1 & 3 & 5 \end{vmatrix} = -3 \begin{vmatrix} 1 & -\frac{4}{3} & \frac{8}{3} \\ 0 & 1 & 2 \\ 0 & 0 & -\frac{19}{3} \end{vmatrix} = 19.$$

It is of course possible to avoid taking out the factor 3 in (ii). But we emphasize that the method is systematic and could be programmed for use on a computer. □

Problem 2.9 (i) Prove that if A is an $n \times n$ matrix and λ is a number then $|\lambda A| = \lambda^n|A|$. (ii) If A is skew-symmetric and n is odd prove that $|A| = 0$.

Solution. (i) This follows at once from property D2 as we may take a factor λ from each row of λA.

(ii) Because $A' = -A$ we can use Problem 2.4 and (i) of the present problem to obtain $|A| = |A'| = |-A| = (-1)^n|A| = -|A|$ and therefore $|A| = 0$. $\qquad\square$

Problem 2.10 Prove that

$$\begin{vmatrix} 1 & 1 & 1 \\ a & b & c \\ a^2 & b^2 & c^2 \end{vmatrix} = (a-b)(b-c)(c-a).$$

Solution. We use the remainder theorem from elementary algebra. The determinant of the given matrix is a polynomial of degree 3 in a,b,c and is zero when $a = b$, $b = c$ or $c = a$. For in each case the matrix has two equal columns. Consequently the remainder theorem shows that the determinant is equal to $\lambda(a-b)(b-c)(c-a)$ where λ is a number. It follows from the definition (2.1) that the coefficient of the term in bc^2 is 1 and so $\lambda = 1$.

The problem can be generalized in an obvious way for an $n \times n$ matrix with n variables $a, b, \ldots, k$. The corresponding determinant is called Vandermonde's determinant. $\qquad\square$

Problem 2.11 Prove that

$$\begin{vmatrix} a & b & c \\ c & a & b \\ b & c & a \end{vmatrix} = (a+b+c)(a+\omega b+\omega^2 c)(a+\omega^2 b+\omega c)$$

where ω is the complex number $\exp(2\pi i/3)$.

Solution. Let τ be any complex number such that $\tau^3 = 1$. We add to the first column of the given matrix τ times the second column and τ^2 times the third column. These operations do not alter the determinant of the matrix and so

$$\begin{vmatrix} a & b & c \\ c & a & b \\ b & c & a \end{vmatrix} = \begin{vmatrix} a+\tau b+\tau^2 c & b & c \\ c+\tau a+\tau^2 b & a & b \\ b+\tau c+\tau^2 a & c & a \end{vmatrix}.$$

Using the relation $\tau^3 = 1$ we can obtain $c+\tau a+\tau^2 b = \tau(a+\tau b+\tau^2 c)$, $b+\tau c+\tau^2 a = \tau^2(a+\tau b+\tau^2 c)$ and it follows that $a+\tau b+\tau^2 c$ is a factor of the determinant. There are three factors corresponding to the

18

values $\tau = 1$, $\tau = \exp(2\pi i/3) = \omega$ and $\tau = \exp(4\pi i/3) = \omega^2$. Consequently, as the determinant is a polynomial of degree 3 in a,b and c it is equal to $\lambda(a+b+c)(a+\omega b+\omega^2 c)(a+\omega^2 b+\omega c)$, where λ is a number. It follows from the definition (2.1) that the coefficient of the term in a^3 is 1 and so $\lambda = 1$.

The problem can be generalized in an obvious way for an $n \times n$ matrix with n variables $a, b, \ldots, k$. Such a matrix is called a circulant matrix. $\qquad\square$

Problem 2.12 A and B are 2×2 matrices. Prove that $|AB| = |A||B|$.
   Solution. From the definition of matrix multiplication

$$|AB| = \begin{vmatrix} a_{11}b_{11}+a_{12}b_{21} & a_{11}b_{12}+a_{12}b_{22} \\ a_{21}b_{11}+a_{22}b_{21} & a_{21}b_{12}+a_{22}b_{22} \end{vmatrix}.$$

By an application of property D3 this determinant can be written as

$$\begin{vmatrix} a_{11}b_{11} & a_{11}b_{12} \\ a_{21}b_{11}+a_{22}b_{21} & a_{21}b_{12}+a_{22}b_{22} \end{vmatrix} + \begin{vmatrix} a_{12}b_{21} & a_{12}b_{22} \\ a_{21}b_{11}+a_{22}b_{21} & a_{21}b_{12}+a_{22}b_{22} \end{vmatrix}$$

and each of these determinants can be expressed as a sum in a similar way. We remove obvious factors from the rows and use Problem 2.6 to show that two of the four determinants are zero. Then using property D1 we combine the remaining two to give

$$|AB| = (a_{11}a_{22}-a_{12}a_{21})\begin{vmatrix} b_{11} & b_{12} \\ b_{21} & b_{22} \end{vmatrix} = |A||B|.$$

The statement and solution of Problem 2.12 extend to square matrices of any order. $\qquad\square$

2.4 Cofactors and the Inverse of a Square Matrix   Consider an element a_{ij} in a matrix A of order $n \times n$. The terms involving a_{ij} in the definition (2.1) can be written as $a_{ij}A_{ij}$ where A_{ij} does not involve any elements from the ith row or the jth column. For example, if A is of order 3×3 we can see from the solution to Problem 2.3 that $A_{23} = a_{12}a_{31}-a_{11}a_{32}$. A_{ij} is called the *cofactor* of a_{ij} with respect to A.

We can expand $|A|$ along any given row of A in terms of the cofactors of that row. That is if the given row is the ith row then

$$|A| = \sum_{j=1}^{n} a_{ij}A_{ij}. \qquad (2.2)$$

This is because each product in equation (2.1) contains just one element

19

from the ith row. The same argument applies to columns so that we can also expand along any given column. The expansion along the kth column is

$$|A| = \sum_{h=1}^{n} a_{hk} A_{hk}. \tag{2.3}$$

Problem 2.13 Let $A = [a_{ij}]$ be a matrix of order $n \times n$ and let A_{ij} denote the cofactor of a_{ij}. Prove that for $h \neq k$

$$\sum_{j=1}^{n} a_{hj} A_{kj} = 0 \tag{2.4}$$

$$\sum_{j=1}^{n} a_{jh} A_{jk} = 0 \tag{2.5}$$

Solution. To prove the first equality consider the matrix B which is obtained from A by replacing the kth row of A by the hth row. The hth and kth rows of B are the same and therefore (Problem 2.6) $|B| = 0$. Consequently the expansion of $|B|$ along the kth row gives $\sum_{j=1}^{n} b_{kj} B_{kj} = 0$. The cofactor B_{kj} of b_{kj} does not depend on the elements in the kth row and so $B_{kj} = A_{kj}$. Because $b_{kj} = a_{hj}(j = 1, \ldots, n)$ we obtain $\sum_{j=1}^{n} a_{hj} A_{kj} = 0$.

The second equality can be derived in a similar way from an expansion of the matrix obtained from A by replacing the kth column of A by the hth. $\qquad \square$

Problem 2.14 Let A denote a square matrix. Prove that (i) if A has an inverse then $|A| \neq 0$, (ii) if $|A| \neq 0$ then A has an inverse, (iii) if $AB = I$ then B is the inverse of A.

Solution. We recall from Problem 1.11 that A has at most one inverse. To solve (i) we let A^{-1} be the matrix inverse to A so that $AA^{-1} = I$ and therefore $|AA^{-1}| = 1$. Using the extension of Problem 2.12 we find that $|A||A^{-1}| = 1$ and consequently $|A| \neq 0$.

To solve (ii) we form the matrix $[A_{ij}]$ of cofactors. The transpose of this matrix is called the *adjugate matrix* of A and is written as adj A. The equations (2.2) and (2.4) can be expressed together as A adj $A = |A|I$ and the equations (2.3) and (2.5) as adj $A \cdot A = |A|I$ where I is a unit matrix. It follows that if $|A| \neq 0$ then the matrix $A^{-1} = (|A|)^{-1}$ adj A is a matrix inverse to A.

To solve (iii) we again use the extension of Problem 2.12 to show that

20

$|A\|B| = |AB| = 1$. Therefore $|A| \neq 0$ and A has an inverse A^{-1} defined as in part (ii). Consequently $B = (A^{-1}A)B = A^{-1}(AB) = A^{-1}I = A^{-1}$. We remark that (iii) can be used to shorten some solutions in Chapter I. $\qquad\square$

A square matrix is *non-singular* if its determinant is non-zero. Problem 2.14 shows that a square matrix has an inverse if and only if it is non-singular.

Problem 2.15   Show that if A is a non-singular 2×2 matrix then the formula for A^{-1} given in Problem 2.14 (ii) agrees with the formula given in 1.4.

Solution.   Since $|A| = a_{11}a_{22} - a_{12}a_{21}$ the matrix of cofactors is
$\begin{bmatrix} a_{22} & -a_{21} \\ -a_{12} & a_{11} \end{bmatrix}$ and therefore
$$ A^{-1} = (|A|)^{-1}\,\mathrm{adj}\,A = (|A|)^{-1}\begin{bmatrix} a_{22} & -a_{12} \\ -a_{21} & a_{11} \end{bmatrix}. $$

This is the same formula as that in 1.4. $\qquad\square$

We explain a method for calculating the cofactors. Let a_{ij} be an element in a matrix A of order $n \times n$. We obtain a submatrix of A of order $(n-1) \times (n-1)$ by omitting the row and column containing a_{ij}. The determinant of this submatrix is called the *minor* of a_{ij}. The cofactor A_{ij} is related to the minor by
$$ A_{ij} = (-1)^{i+j} \times (\text{minor of } a_{ij}). \tag{2.6} $$
For example, if A is of order 3×3 then the minor of a_{23} is the determinant $\begin{vmatrix} a_{11} & a_{12} \\ a_{31} & a_{32} \end{vmatrix} = a_{11}a_{32} - a_{12}a_{31}$. We have previously noted that $A_{23} = a_{12}a_{31} - a_{11}a_{32}$ and so we can verify the relation (2.6) in this particular case. Perhaps the easiest way to remember the sign $(-1)^{i+j}$ is to notice that it varies with the position of a_{ij} according to the scheme
$$ \begin{bmatrix} + & - & + & \cdot & \cdot \\ - & + & - & \cdot & \cdot \\ \cdot & \cdot & \cdot & \cdot & \cdot \end{bmatrix} $$
where each horizontal or vertical move involves a change of sign.

Problem 2.16   Calculate the determinant
$$ \begin{vmatrix} 0 & 1 & 2 \\ 3 & -4 & 8 \\ 1 & 3 & 5 \end{vmatrix} $$

  (i) by an expansion along the first row

  (ii) by an expansion along the second column.

Solution. (i) The minors of the elements along the first row are respectively $\begin{vmatrix} -4 & 8 \\ 3 & 5 \end{vmatrix}$, $\begin{vmatrix} 3 & 8 \\ 1 & 5 \end{vmatrix}$, $\begin{vmatrix} 3 & -4 \\ 1 & 3 \end{vmatrix}$. The corresponding cofactors are therefore -44, -7, 13 and the determinant is $(0)(-38)+(1)(-7)+(2)(13) = 19$.

(ii) The cofactors of the elements in the second column are respectively $-7, -2, 6$. Consequently the determinant is $(1)(-7)+(-4)(-2)+(3)(6) = 19$.

This method of calculating a determinant is not recommended for matrices of order greater than 3×3.   □

Problem 2.17   Calculate the inverse of the matrix

$$A = \begin{bmatrix} 1 & 1 & 1 \\ 2 & 1 & 2 \\ 3 & 2 & 4 \end{bmatrix}.$$

Solution. The matrix of cofactors is

$$\begin{bmatrix} 0 & -2 & 1 \\ -2 & 1 & 1 \\ 1 & 0 & -1 \end{bmatrix}.$$

We calculate $|A|$ by an expansion along the first row as $(1)(0)+(1)(-2)+(1)(1) = -1$. Therefore

$$A^{-1} = (|A|)^{-1}\text{adj } A = \begin{bmatrix} 0 & 2 & -1 \\ 2 & -1 & 0 \\ -1 & -1 & 1 \end{bmatrix}.$$

This method of calculating the inverse of a matrix is not recommended for matrices of order greater than 3×3.   □

Problem 2.18 (Cramer's Rule) A is a non-singular matrix of order $n \times n$. Prove that the solutions to the equations $Ax = h$ are $x_i = (|A|)^{-1}|A_i|$, $i = 1,\ldots,n$ where the matrix A_i is obtained from A by replacing the ith column by the column vector h.

Solution. A has an inverse A^{-1} and therefore the solutions are given by $x = A^{-1}h = (|A|)^{-1}\text{adj } A \cdot h$. Consequently

$$x_i = (|A|)^{-1} \sum_{j=1}^{n} A_{ji} h_j = (|A|)^{-1}|A_i|$$

because $\sum_{j=1}^{n} A_{ji} h_j$ is the expansion of the determinant $|A_i|$ along the ith column. □

Problem 2.19 Use Cramer's Rule to find the value of x_2 from the system of linear equations $x_1 - x_2 + 2x_3 = 1$, $3x_1 - 4x_2 + 8x_3 = 0$, $x_1 + 3x_2 + 5x_3 = -1$.

Solution. With the notation of Problem 2.18, $x_2 = (|A|)^{-1}|A_2|$ where

$$A = \begin{bmatrix} 1 & -1 & 2 \\ 3 & -4 & 8 \\ 1 & 3 & 5 \end{bmatrix}, \qquad A_2 = \begin{bmatrix} 1 & 1 & 2 \\ 3 & 0 & 8 \\ 1 & -1 & 5 \end{bmatrix}.$$

A calculation of the determinants gives $|A| = -11$, $|A_2| = -5$ and so $x_2 = \frac{5}{11}$. □

Problem 2.20 (Cauchy's Theorem) A is an $n \times n$ matrix where $n > 1$. Prove that $|\text{adj } A| = (|A|)^{n-1}$.

Solution. In the solution to Problem 2.14 we obtained

$$A \text{ adj } A = |A| I \qquad (2.7)$$

and so $|A| |\text{adj } A| = |A \text{ adj } A| = (|A|)^n$. If A is non-singular it follows that $|\text{adj } A| = (|A|)^{n-1}$. The result is trivial if $A = O$ and we are left with the case $|A| = 0$ but $A \neq O$. We must prove that $|\text{adj } A| = 0$ and this is a consequence of the relation (2.7) which reduces to $A \text{ adj } A = O$. For $|\text{adj } A| \neq 0$ implies that $\text{adj } A$ has an inverse and therefore $A = O$. □

Problem 2.21 A square matrix A is partitioned as $A = \begin{bmatrix} B & D \\ O & C \end{bmatrix}$

where B, C are square matrices. Prove that $|A| = |B||C|$.

Solution. We use I_s to denote the unit matrix of order $s \times s$ and suppose that A is of order $n \times n$ and that B is of order $r \times r$. We put $E = \begin{bmatrix} I_r & D \\ O & C \end{bmatrix}$ and $F = \begin{bmatrix} B & O \\ O & I_{n-r} \end{bmatrix}$. By expanding along the first column we find that $|E| = \begin{vmatrix} I_{r-1} & D_1 \\ O & C \end{vmatrix}$ and, after r successive expansions of this kind we obtain $|E| = |C|$. A similar succession of expansions of determinants along their last rows leads to $|F| = |B|$. Because $A = EF$ it follows from the extension of Problem 2.12 that $|A| = |E||F| = |B||C|$.

23

Problem 2.21 extends to a square matrix partitioned into a triangular form with any number of square submatrices along the diagonal. The determinant of such a matrix is equal to the product of the determinants of the diagonal submatrices. ☐

Problem 2.22 $A = [a_{ij}]$ is a real 3×3 matrix and O is the origin of rectangular cartesian coordinates in euclidean space. Let P_j ($j = 1, 2, 3$) be the point of coordinates (a_{1j}, a_{2j}, a_{3j}). Prove that the volume of the parallelepiped spanned by OP_1, OP_2, OP_3 is equal to the absolute value of $|A|$. Deduce that

$$|A|^2 \leqslant \prod_{j=1}^{3} (a_{1j}^2 + a_{2j}^2 + a_{3j}^2).$$

Solution. The parallelepiped spanned by the position vectors $\mathbf{OP_1}$, $\mathbf{OP_2}$, $\mathbf{OP_3}$ is the set of all points P such that $\mathbf{OP} = \alpha\mathbf{OP_1} + \beta\mathbf{OP_2} + \gamma\mathbf{OP_3}$ where $0 \leqslant \alpha, \beta, \gamma \leqslant 1$. The volume of this figure is equal to the product of the area of a base parallelogram with the perpendicular height. The area of the base parallelogram spanned by $\mathbf{OP_2}$, $\mathbf{OP_3}$ is equal to the magnitude of the vector product $\mathbf{OP_2} \wedge \mathbf{OP_3}$. Consequently the volume of the parallelepiped is the absolute value of the triple scalar product $\mathbf{OP_1} \cdot (\mathbf{OP_2} \wedge \mathbf{OP_3})$. A calculation of this product in terms of the components of the position vectors shows that it is equal to $|A|$. The volume of the parallelepiped is $\leqslant$ the product of the lengths OP_1, OP_2, OP_3. Therefore $|A|^2 \leqslant (OP_1)^2 (OP_2)^2 (OP_3)^2 = \prod_{j=1}^{3} (a_{1j}^2 + a_{2j}^2 + a_{3j}^2)$. ☐

Problem 2.23 (i) A is an $n \times n$ matrix. Show that $\partial(|A|)/\partial a_{ij} = A_{ij}$ and, if all the elements of A are functions of a variable t, deduce that

$$\frac{d}{dt}(|A|) = \sum_{i,j=1}^{n} A_{ij} \frac{d}{dt}(a_{ij}).$$

(ii) Prove that the determinant of the matrix

$$T = \begin{bmatrix} 1 & 1 & 1 \\ t+a & t+b & t+c \\ t^2+a^2 & t^2+b^2 & t^2+c^2 \end{bmatrix}$$

is independent of t.

Solution. (i) The terms in the definition (2.1) which involve a_{ij} are $a_{ij} A_{ij}$ where A_{ij} does not contain a_{ij}. Consequently $\partial(|A|)/\partial a_{ij} = A_{ij}$. If all the elements of A are functions of t we can use the Chain Rule of the differential calculus to obtain

$$\frac{d}{dt}(|A|) = \sum_{i,\,j=1}^{n} \frac{\partial(|A|)}{\partial a_{ij}} \cdot \frac{d}{dt}(a_{ij}) = \sum_{i,\,j=1}^{n} A_{ij} \frac{d}{dt}(a_{ij}).$$

(ii) Expressed as $d(|A|)/dt = \sum_{i=1}^{n} [\sum_{j=1}^{n}(da_{ij}/dt)A_{ij}]$ the formula in (i) shows that $d(|A|)/dt$ is equal to the sum of the determinants of n matrices obtained from A by replacing the elements in the ith row, $i = 1,\ldots,n$ with their derivatives.

We apply this remark to T and find that

$$\frac{d}{dt}(|T|) = \begin{vmatrix} 0 & 0 & 0 \\ t+a & t+b & t+c \\ t^2+a^2 & t^2+b^2 & t^2+c^2 \end{vmatrix} + \begin{vmatrix} 1 & 1 & 1 \\ 1 & 1 & 1 \\ t^2+a^2 & t^2+b^2 & t^2+c^2 \end{vmatrix}$$

$$+ \begin{vmatrix} 1 & 1 & 1 \\ t+a & t+b & t+c \\ 2t & 2t & 2t \end{vmatrix}.$$

All three determinants are obviously zero and therefore $|T|$ is independent of t. We can find the actual value of $|T|$ by calculating the determinant with $t = 0$. This has been done in Problem 2.10. $\square$

EXERCISES

1. Write out all the non-zero terms in the definition (2.1) for a skew-symmetric matrix A of order 4×4. Show that $|A| = (a_{12}a_{34} - a_{13}a_{24} + a_{14}a_{23})^2$.

2. Prove that if A is a complex matrix then $|\bar{A}| = \overline{|A|}$. Deduce that the determinant of a hermitian matrix is real. What can you say about the determinant of a skew-hermitian matrix?

3. Let

$$A = \begin{bmatrix} 1 & 2 & 1 \\ -1 & 3 & 0 \\ 0 & 1 & -1 \end{bmatrix}.$$

Calculate $|A|$ (i) by an expansion along the third column, (ii) by an expansion along the second row. Find also the inverse matrix A^{-1}.

4. Use Cramer's Rule to find the value of x_3 from the system of linear equations $x_1 - x_2 + 2x_3 - x_4 = 1, \; -2x_1 + 3x_2 - 6x_3 + 2x_4 = -1, \; -x_1 + x_2 - 3x_3 - x_4 = 1, \; 2x_1 - x_2 + 3x_3 + x_4 = 1$.

25

5. Factorise the determinants of the following matrices:

$$\begin{bmatrix} 1 & a & bc \\ 1 & b & ca \\ 1 & c & ab \end{bmatrix}, \quad \begin{bmatrix} 1 & 1 & 1 \\ a & b & c \\ a^3 & b^3 & c^3 \end{bmatrix}, \quad \begin{bmatrix} a & b & c \\ -c & a & b \\ -b & -c & a \end{bmatrix}.$$

(The third matrix is a skew-circulant and be factorised by using the roots of the equation $\tau^3 = -1$.)

6. (i) Express the matrix

$$\begin{bmatrix} b^2+c^2 & ab & ca \\ ab & c^2+a^2 & bc \\ ca & bc & a^2+b^2 \end{bmatrix}$$

as a product $A'A$ where A is of order 3×3 and hence show that its determinant is $4a^2b^2c^2$.

(ii) A is a non-singular matrix of order $n \times n$ where $n > 1$. Show that adj(adj A) $= |A|^{n-2}A$.

Chapter 3

Elementary Transformations of a Matrix

3.1 Elementary Transformations and Linear Equations A good method of solving simultaneous linear equations is by a systematic elimination of the unknowns. This involves certain operations on the matrix of coefficients called elementary transformations. An *elementary row transformation* is one of the operations

    T1. the interchange of two rows
    T2. the multiplication of one row by a non-zero number
    T3. the addition of a multiple of one row to another.

An *elementary column transformation* is defined in a similar way. A matrix is in *echelon form* if it can be partitioned as $\begin{bmatrix} \varLambda & C \\ O & O \end{bmatrix}$ where $\varLambda$ is an upper triangular matrix with 1's along the diagonal.

Problem 3.1   Transform

$$\text{(i)}\begin{bmatrix} 1 & -1 & 2 \\ 3 & -4 & 8 \\ 1 & 3 & 5 \end{bmatrix} \quad \text{(ii)}\begin{bmatrix} 1 & 2 & 3 & 4 \\ 1 & 2 & 4 & 5 \\ 2 & 4 & 5 & 7 \end{bmatrix}$$

into echelon form by using elementary row transformations and column interchanges.

   Solution. We carry out the following transformations:

  (i) (row 2) − 3(row 1), (row 3) − (row 1), $(-1) \times$ (row 2), (row 3) − 4(row 2), $(1/11) \times$ (row 3).

  (ii) (row 2) − (row 1), (row 3) − 2(row 1), interchange columns 2 and 4, (row 3) + (row 2).

The corresponding echelon forms are

$$\begin{bmatrix} 1 & -1 & 2 \\ 0 & 1 & -2 \\ 0 & 0 & 1 \end{bmatrix}, \quad \begin{bmatrix} 1 & 4 & 3 & 2 \\ 0 & 1 & 1 & 0 \\ 0 & 0 & 0 & 0 \end{bmatrix}. \qquad \square$$

Any matrix A can be reduced to echelon form by the methods of Problem 3.1 and this fact is important in the solution of the linear equations $Ax = h$. To effect the solution we reduce A to echelon form by elementary row transformations and column interchanges and carry out the same operations on the *augmented matrix* $[A\,h]$. We obtain a new matrix $[B\,k]$ where B is an echelon form of A. This reduced matrix determines a reduced set of equations $By = k$ where the unknowns $y_1, y_2, \ldots$ are the unknowns $x_1, x_2, \ldots$ but in a different order determined by the column interchanges used. The reduced set of equations has the same solutions as the original set and is very easy to solve.

Problem 3.2 Solve the simultaneous equations
$$x_1 - x_2 + 2x_3 = 1, \quad 3x_1 - 4x_2 + 8x_3 = 0, \quad x_1 + 3x_2 + 5x_3 = -1.$$

Solution. The matrix of coefficients in these equations is the matrix in part (i) of Problem 3.1. We apply to the augmented matrix the transformations given in the solution to that problem and obtain
$$\begin{bmatrix} 1 & -1 & 2 & 1 \\ 0 & 1 & -2 & 3 \\ 0 & 0 & 1 & -\frac{14}{11} \end{bmatrix}.$$

As no column interchanges have been used the reduced set of equations is
$$x_1 - x_2 + 2x_3 = 1, \quad x_2 - 2x_3 = 3, \quad x_3 = -\tfrac{14}{11}.$$
This set has the same solutions as the original set and is easily solved. It has the unique solution $x_3 = -\tfrac{14}{11}$, $x_2 = \tfrac{5}{11}$, $x_1 = 4$.

In general the method used in this problem is much better than Cramer's Rule. $\qquad\square$

Problem 3.3 Prove that the simultaneous equations
$$x_1 + 2x_2 + 3x_3 + 4x_4 = h_1, \quad x_1 + 2x_2 + 4x_3 + 5x_4 = h_2,$$
$$2x_1 + 4x_2 + 5x_3 + 7x_4 = h_3$$
are *consistent* (i.e. have solutions) if and only if $3h_1 - h_2 - h_3 = 0$. If this condition is satisfied show that there is an infinite number of solutions.

Solution. The matrix of coefficients is the matrix in part (ii) of Problem 3.1. We apply to the augmented matrix the transformations given in the solution to that problem and obtain
$$\begin{bmatrix} 1 & 4 & 3 & 2 & h_1 \\ 0 & 1 & 1 & 0 & h_2 - h_1 \\ 0 & 0 & 0 & 0 & h_3 + h_2 - 3h_1 \end{bmatrix}.$$

Columns 2 and 4 have been interchanged in the reduction and therefore the reduced set of equations is

$$x_1 + 4x_4 + 3x_3 + 2x_2 = h_1$$
$$0x_1 + x_4 + x_3 + 0x_2 = h_2 - h_1$$
$$0x_1 + 0x_4 + 0x_3 + 0x_2 = h_3 + h_2 - 3h_1 .$$

There are no values of $x_1, \ldots, x_4$ which satisfy these equations unless $h_3 + h_2 - 3h_1 = 0$. But if this condition is satisfied we obtain an infinite number of solutions by giving x_2 and x_3 arbitrary values. Explicitly,

$$x_2 = \alpha, \quad x_3 = \beta, \quad x_4 = h_2 - h_1 - \beta, \quad x_1 = 5h_1 - 4h_2 - 2\alpha + \beta$$

is a solution for all numbers α, β. $\qquad\square$

3.2 The Rank of a Matrix A given system of linear equations can have a unique solution or no solution or an infinity of solutions. Conditions for these possibilities can be expressed in terms of the rank of a matrix. Consider the set of all the square submatrices of a matrix A. If a non-singular submatrix of highest order in this set is of order $r \times r$ then A is said to have *rank* r. We note some easy consequences of this definition. If A is of order $m \times n$ then $r \leqslant m$ and $r \leqslant n$. If A is of order $n \times n$ then A is non-singular if and only if $r = n$. A less trivial fact is that rank A = rank A'. This follows from Problem 2.4.

Problem 3.4   Find the rank of the matrix

$$A = \begin{bmatrix} 1 & 2 & 3 & 4 \\ 1 & 2 & 4 & 5 \\ 2 & 4 & 5 & 7 \end{bmatrix}.$$

Solution. The solution is only intended to make clear the definition of rank and the method used is not a practical one. The 3×3 submatrices of A are

$$\begin{bmatrix} 1 & 2 & 3 \\ 1 & 2 & 4 \\ 2 & 4 & 5 \end{bmatrix}, \quad \begin{bmatrix} 1 & 2 & 4 \\ 1 & 2 & 5 \\ 2 & 4 & 7 \end{bmatrix}, \quad \begin{bmatrix} 1 & 3 & 4 \\ 1 & 4 & 5 \\ 2 & 5 & 7 \end{bmatrix}, \quad \begin{bmatrix} 2 & 3 & 4 \\ 2 & 4 & 5 \\ 4 & 5 & 7 \end{bmatrix}$$

and these are all singular. The submatrix $\begin{bmatrix} 1 & 3 \\ 1 & 4 \end{bmatrix}$ is non-singular and therefore rank $A = 2$. $\qquad\square$

Problem 3.5 A matrix M is partitioned as $\begin{bmatrix} A & B \\ O & O \end{bmatrix}$ where A is a non-singular matrix of order $r \times r$. Prove that rank $M = r$.

Solution. A is a non-singular submatrix of M and therefore rank $M \geqslant r$. Any submatrix of M of order $s \times s$ with $s > r$ contains a zero row and is therefore singular. Consequently rank $M = r$. $\qquad\square$

Problem 3.6 A is a matrix such that all the submatrices of order $s \times s$ are singular. Prove that rank $A < s$.

Solution. Expansion along a row (or column) shows that any submatrix of A of order $(s+1) \times (s+1)$ is singular. The argument can be repeated to show that any submatrix of order $n \times n$ $(n > s+1)$ is singular. Consequently rank $A < s$. $\qquad\square$

Problem 3.7 Prove that an elementary transformation does not alter the rank of a matrix.

Solution. Let B be a matrix obtained from a matrix A of rank r by an elementary transformation. Because the $(r+1) \times (r+1)$ submatrices of A are singular it is not difficult to show that, for each type of transformation, any $(r+1) \times (r+1)$ submatrix of B is also singular. Therefore rank $B \leqslant r =$ rank A. But A can be obtained from B by an elementary transformation and consequently rank $A \leqslant$ rank B. It follows that rank $A =$ rank B. $\qquad\square$

Problem 3.8 Find the rank of the matrix

$$A = \begin{bmatrix} 1 & 1 & 2 & -3 & 4 \\ 0 & 2 & 4 & -6 & 6 \\ 1 & 3 & 4 & -5 & 8 \\ 1 & 3 & 5 & -7 & 9 \end{bmatrix}.$$

Solution. Suppose that A is reduced to echelon form. It follows from Problems 3.5 and 3.7 that rank $A = r$ where $r \times r$ is the order of the upper triangular matrix in the echelon form. The following operations effect the reduction and show that $r = 3$: (row 3) $-$ (row 1), (row 4) $-$ (row 1), $\frac{1}{2} \times$ (row 2), (row 3) $-$ 2(row 2), (row 4) $-$ 2(row 2), $-(-\frac{1}{2}) \times$ (row 3), (row 4) $+$ (row 3). $\qquad\square$

Problem 3.9 Prove that the equations $Ax = h$ are consistent if and only if rank $A =$ rank $[A\, h]$.

Solution. We have already explained that the equations $Ax = h$ have exactly the same solutions as the reduced set $By = k$ where B is an echelon form of A, $[B\, k]$ has been obtained from $[A\, h]$ by elementary transformations and the unknowns $y_1, y_2, \ldots$ are the unknowns $x_1, x_2, \ldots$ but possibly in a different order. Let $m \times n$ be the order of A and put rank $A = r$. Problem 3.7 shows that rank $B = r$ and so $[B\,k] = \begin{bmatrix} \varDelta & C & p \\ O & O & q \end{bmatrix}$ where $k = \begin{bmatrix} p \\ q \end{bmatrix}$ and where $\varDelta$ is an upper triangular matrix of order $r \times r$ with 1's along the diagonal. The reduced set is therefore

$$
\begin{array}{rcl}
y_1 + \cdot \quad \cdot \quad \cdot & = & p_1 \\
y_2 + \cdot \quad \cdot \quad \cdot & = & p_2 \\
\cdot \quad \cdot \quad \cdot \qquad \cdot \quad \cdot \quad \cdot & & \\
y_r + \cdot \quad \cdot \qquad \cdot & = & p_r \\
0y_1 + 0y_2 + \cdot \quad \cdot \quad \cdot \quad \cdot \quad +0y_n & = & q_1 \\
\cdot \quad \cdot \quad \cdot \quad \cdot \quad \cdot \quad \cdot \qquad \cdot \quad \cdot \quad \cdot & & \\
0y_1 + 0y_2 + \qquad \qquad +0y_n & = & q_{m-r}.
\end{array}
$$

These equations (and consequently the equations $Ax = h$) have solutions if and only if $q = O$. It is not difficult to see that $q = O$ if and only if rank $[B\,k] = r$. But Problem 3.7 shows that rank $[B\,k] =$ rank $[A\,h]$ and so $q = 0$ if and only if rank $[A\,h] = r =$ rank A.

We note that if the equations $Ax = h$ are consistent then they have a unique solution when $r = n$ but an infinity of solutions when $r < n$. Indeed if $r < n$ the $n-r$ unknowns $y_{r+1}, \ldots, y_n$ can be given arbitrary values. $\qquad\square$

Problem 3.10 A is a matrix of order $m \times n$. Prove that the homogeneous equations $Ax = O$ have non-trivial solutions if and only if rank $A < n$.

Solution. A *non-trivial* solution is a solution different from $x_1 = x_2 = \ldots = x_n = 0$. Referring to Problem 3.9 we see that the reduced set is (apart from equations $0 = 0$)

$$
\begin{array}{rcl}
y_1 + \cdot \quad \cdot \quad \cdot & = & 0 \\
y_2 + \cdot \quad \cdot \quad \cdot & = & 0 \\
\cdot \quad \cdot \quad \cdot \qquad \cdot \quad \cdot \quad \cdot & & \\
y_r + \cdot \quad \cdot \quad \cdot & = & 0
\end{array}
$$

This set of equations has non-trivial solutions if and only if r is less than the number of unknowns. In the very important special case when A is a square matrix it follows that the equations $Ax = O$ have non-trivial solutions if and only if $|A| = 0$. $\qquad\square$

Problem 3.11 Show that the equations
$$x_2 + 2x_3 = 0, \qquad -x_1 + x_3 = 0, \qquad -2x_1 - x_2 = 0$$
have non-trivial solutions and find these solutions.

Solution. The matrix of coefficients is skew-symmetric of order 3×3. Its determinant is therefore zero and the equations have non-trivial solutions. The elementary transformations: interchange rows 1 and 2, $(-1) \times$(row 1), (row 3)+2(row 1), (row 3)+(row 2), lead to the reduced set of equations

$$x_1 - x_3 = 0, \qquad x_2 + 2x_3 = 0, \qquad 0 = 0.$$

These have the solutions $x_3 = \alpha$, $x_2 = -2\alpha$, $x_1 = \alpha$ where α is any number. ☐

Problem 3.12 Show that just one of the two sets of linear equations (i) $Ax = h$ (ii) $A'y = 0, h'y = 1$ is consistent.

Solution. Necessary and sufficient conditions for consistency are in (i) rank A = rank $[A\ h]$ and in (ii), after transposing the matrices involved, rank $[A\ h]$ = rank $\begin{bmatrix} A & h \\ O & 1 \end{bmatrix}$. The inequalities rank $A \leqslant$ rank $[A\ h] \leqslant$ rank $\begin{bmatrix} A & h \\ O & 1 \end{bmatrix}$ are obvious and it is not difficult to see that rank $\begin{bmatrix} A & h \\ O & 1 \end{bmatrix}$ = rank $A + 1$. Because the rank of a matrix is an integer it follows that either rank $[A\ h]$ = rank A or rank $[A\ h]$ = rank $\begin{bmatrix} A & h \\ O & 1 \end{bmatrix}$. ☐

3.3 Elementary Matrices An elementary row (column) transformation can be carried out by pre(post)multiplying by a matrix obtained from a unit matrix by the same elementary transformation. Matrices constructed in this way are called *elementary matrices*. Any such matrix can be constructed both by a row and by a column transformation.

An elementary matrix has an inverse matrix. Indeed the inverse matrix is the elementary matrix which represents the inverse elementary transformation.

A matrix is in *normal form* if it can be partitioned as $\begin{bmatrix} I & O \\ O & O \end{bmatrix}$ where I is a unit matrix. Any matrix A can be reduced to a normal form by a succession of elementary row and column transformations. Problems 3.5 and 3.7 show that the order of I in the normal form is $r \times r$ where $r = \text{rank } A$.

Problem 3.13 Find the elementary matrices which effect the following elementary transformations on the matrix $\begin{bmatrix} a & b & c \\ d & e & f \end{bmatrix}$. (i) (row 1)+ λ(row 2) (ii) interchange columns 1 and 3 (iii) $\lambda \times$(row 2), $\lambda \neq 0$ (iv) (column 3)+λ(column 2).

Verify the answer to (iv) by a calculation.

Solution. (i) $\begin{bmatrix} 1 & \lambda \\ 0 & 1 \end{bmatrix}$ (ii) $\begin{bmatrix} 0 & 0 & 1 \\ 0 & 1 & 0 \\ 1 & 0 & 0 \end{bmatrix}$ (iii) $\begin{bmatrix} 1 & 0 \\ 0 & \lambda \end{bmatrix}$ (iv) $\begin{bmatrix} 1 & 0 & 0 \\ 0 & 1 & \lambda \\ 0 & 0 & 1 \end{bmatrix}$.

We verify (iv) by $\begin{bmatrix} a & b & c \\ d & e & f \end{bmatrix} \begin{bmatrix} 1 & 0 & 0 \\ 0 & 1 & \lambda \\ 0 & 0 & 1 \end{bmatrix} = \begin{bmatrix} a & b & c+\lambda b \\ d & e & f+\lambda e \end{bmatrix}$.

$\square$

Problem 3.14 Find the elementary transformations which are carried out by the following elementary matrices when they (a) premultiply (b) postmultiply a given matrix. Also find the inverse matrices.

(i) $\begin{bmatrix} 1 & 0 & 0 \\ 0 & 1 & 0 \\ \lambda & 0 & 1 \end{bmatrix}$ (ii) $\begin{bmatrix} 0 & 0 & 1 \\ 0 & 1 & 0 \\ 1 & 0 & 0 \end{bmatrix}$ (iii) $\begin{bmatrix} 1 & 0 & 0 \\ 0 & 1 & 0 \\ 0 & 0 & \lambda \end{bmatrix}$, $\lambda \neq 0$.

Solution. (i) (a) (row 3)+λ(row 1). (b) (column 1)+λ(column 3). (ii) (a) interchange rows 1 and 3. (b) interchange columns 1 and 3. (iii) (a) $\lambda \times$(row 3), (b) $\lambda \times$(column 3).

(i) The inverse row transformation is (row 3)$-\lambda$(row 1) and therefore the inverse matrix is

$$\begin{bmatrix} 1 & 0 & 0 \\ 0 & 1 & 0 \\ -\lambda & 0 & 1 \end{bmatrix}.$$

Similarly the matrices inverse to (ii), (iii) are

$$\begin{bmatrix} 0 & 0 & 1 \\ 0 & 1 & 0 \\ 1 & 0 & 0 \end{bmatrix}, \quad \begin{bmatrix} 1 & 0 & 0 \\ 0 & 1 & 0 \\ 0 & 0 & \lambda^{-1} \end{bmatrix}.$$

$\square$

Problem 3.15 Reduce the matrix

$$A = \begin{bmatrix} 1 & 2 & 3 & 4 \\ 1 & 2 & 4 & 5 \\ 2 & 4 & 5 & 7 \end{bmatrix}$$

to a normal form by a succession of elementary transformations.

Solution. In Problem 3.1 A has been reduced to the echelon form

$$\begin{bmatrix} 1 & 4 & 3 & 2 \\ 0 & 1 & 1 & 0 \\ 0 & 0 & 0 & 0 \end{bmatrix}.$$

The elementary transformations (column 2) − 4(column 1), (column 3) − 3(column 1), (column 4) − 2(column 1), (column 3) − (column 2) reduce the echelon form to the normal form

$$\begin{bmatrix} 1 & 0 & 0 & 0 \\ 0 & 1 & 0 & 0 \\ 0 & 0 & 0 & 0 \end{bmatrix}. \qquad \square$$

Problem 3.16 Prove that any non-singular matrix is a product of elementary matrices.

Solution. Let A denote a non-singular matrix and I the unit matrix of the same order. A can be reduced by elementary row and column transformations to the normal form I. Consequently there are elementary matrices $E_1, \ldots, E_p, F_1, \ldots, F_q$ such that $E_1 \ldots E_p A F_1 \ldots F_q = I$. Therefore $A = E_p^{-1} \ldots E_1^{-1} F_q^{-1} \ldots F_1^{-1}$ which is a product of elementary matrices. $\qquad \square$

We remark that conversely any product $P = E_1 \ldots E_p$ of elementary matrices is non-singular. For P has an inverse $E_p^{-1} \ldots E_1^{-1}$. Thus the fact that any matrix B can be reduced to a normal form can be expressed by saying that there are non-singular matrices P, Q such that PBQ is a normal form. $\qquad \square$

Problem 3.17 Prove that multiplication by a non-singular matrix does not alter rank.

Solution. We express the non-singular matrix A as a product $E_1 \ldots E_p$ of elementary matrices. Then, because elementary transformations do not alter rank, rank $AB = $ rank $E_1 \ldots E_p B = $ rank $E_2 \ldots E_p B = \ldots = $ rank B.

A similar argument shows that rank $CA = $ rank C. $\qquad \square$

Problem 3.18 A, B are matrices of orders $m \times n$, $n \times l$ and ranks r, s respectively. Prove that (i) rank $AB \leqslant$ the smallest of r, s (ii) rank $AB \geqslant r+s-n$.

Solution. We prove these inequalities first when A is the normal form $\begin{bmatrix} I_r & 0 \\ 0 & 0 \end{bmatrix}$, I_r being the unit matrix of order $r \times r$. We partition $B = \begin{bmatrix} B_1 \\ B_2 \end{bmatrix}$ where B_1 is of order $r \times l$ and find that $AB = \begin{bmatrix} B_1 \\ 0 \end{bmatrix}$. Consequently rank $AB = $ rank B_1. Therefore rank $AB \leqslant r$ because B_1 has order $r \times l$. Rank $AB \leqslant s$ is also obvious because B_1 is a submatrix of B and therefore rank $B_1 \leqslant $ rank B.

The inequality (ii) needs a little more argument. Consider a non-singular submatrix M of B of order $s \times s$ and suppose that t rows of M are in rows of B_1. These rows must contain a non-singular submatrix of order $t \times t$ and so rank $B_1 \geqslant t$. Because B_2 has $n-r$ rows the number of rows of M which lie in rows of B_1 is at least $s-(n-r) = s+r-n$. Consequently rank $B_1 \geqslant r+s-n$.

To prove the general case we introduce non-singular matrices P, Q such that $PAQ = \begin{bmatrix} I_r & 0 \\ 0 & 0 \end{bmatrix}$. Then, using Problem 3.17, we obtain rank $AB = $ rank $PAB = $ rank $(PAQ)Q^{-1}B$. The inequalities now follow from the special case already proved because rank $Q^{-1}B = $ rank B.

Problem 3.19 Prove that a matrix of rank one is equal to uv' where u and v are column vectors.

Solution. A reduction to normal form of a matrix A of rank one gives $PAQ = \begin{bmatrix} 1 & 0 \\ 0 & 0 \end{bmatrix}$ or $A = P^{-1}\begin{bmatrix} 1 & 0 \\ 0 & 0 \end{bmatrix}Q^{-1}$. Partition P^{-1} as $[u \ X]$ where u is the first column and partition Q^{-1} as $\begin{bmatrix} v' \\ Y \end{bmatrix}$ where v' is the first row.

A calculation shows that $A = uv'$. $\qquad \square$

Elementary transformations can be used in a systematic and practical way to find the inverse of a non-singular matrix. Such a matrix A is a product of elementary matrices and consequently there are elementary matrices $E_1, \ldots, E_p$ such that $E_1 \ldots E_p A = I$. It follows that A can be reduced to I by a sequence of elementary row transformations. But further $A^{-1} = E_1 \ldots E_p = E_1 \ldots E_p I$ and therefore A^{-1} can be obtained by carrying out the same sequence of elementary row transformations on the appropriate unit matrix.

Problem 3.20   Calculate the inverse of the matrix

$$A = \begin{bmatrix} 1 & -2 & -7 & 7 \\ -1 & 2 & 8 & -5 \\ 3 & -4 & -17 & 13 \\ 2 & -2 & -11 & 8 \end{bmatrix}$$

Solution. We list a sequence of elementary row transformations which reduce A to I:

(row 2)+(row 1),   (row 3)−3(row 1),   (row 4)−2(row 1),
interchange rows 2 and 3, $\frac{1}{2}$×(row 2),
(row 4)−2(row 2),   (row 4)+(row 3), $\frac{1}{4}$×(row 4),
(row 3)−2(row 4),   (row 2)+4(row 4),   (row 1)−7(row 4),
(row 2)−2(row 3),   (row 1)+7(row 3),   (row 1)+2(row 2).

The same sequence applied to the unit matrix of order 4×4 gives the inverse matrix

$$A^{-1} = \frac{1}{4} \begin{bmatrix} -6 & 7 & 9 & -5 \\ 2 & 0 & -6 & 8 \\ 0 & 2 & 2 & -2 \\ 2 & 1 & -1 & 1 \end{bmatrix}.$$ $\square$

EXERCISES

1.   (i) Use elementary transformations to solve the system of equations in Exercise 4 of Chapter 2.
   (ii) Put

$$A = \begin{bmatrix} 1 & 1 & 1 & 0 \\ 2 & 1 & -1 & -1 \\ 1 & 3 & 7 & 2 \\ -4 & 0 & 8 & 4 \end{bmatrix}.$$

Show that the equations $Ax = h$ are consistent if and only if $h_3 - 5h_1 + 2h_2 = 0$, $h_4 - 4h_1 + 4h_2 = 0$.

2.   (i) Write out the possible elementary matrices of order 2×2.
   (ii) Express $\begin{bmatrix} 1 & -1 \\ 3 & 2 \end{bmatrix}$ as a product of elementary matrices.

36

3. (i) A, B are matrices of orders $m \times n$, $n \times l$ respectively and both have rank n. Prove that AB has rank n.

(ii) Find a pair of matrices A, B for which both the inequalities in Problem 3.18 are strict.

4. Show that a matrix of rank two can be expressed as $u_1 v_1' + u_2 v_2'$ where u_1, v_1, u_2, v_2 are column vectors. Generalise this result for a matrix of rank r.

5. Use elementary transformations to find the inverse of the matrix

$$\begin{bmatrix} 0 & 1 & 0 & 1 \\ -1 & 0 & 1 & 0 \\ 0 & -1 & 0 & 1 \\ -1 & 0 & -1 & 0 \end{bmatrix}.$$

6. Two column vectors u, v are said to be orthogonal if $u'v = 0$. Use Problem 3.12 to show that the equations $Ax = h$ are consistent if and only if h is orthogonal to all the solutions of the equations $A'y = O$.

Apply this condition to solve Exercise 1(ii).

Chapter 4

Linear Transformations

4.1 Eigenvalues and Eigenvectors   A square matrix A is similar to a square matrix B of the same order if $B = T^{-1}AT$ where T is non-singular. Given A an important problem is to find T so that B is as simple as possible. The solution involves the idea of eigenvalues and eigenvectors.

A scalar μ is an eigenvalue of the square matrix A if there is a non-zero column vector v such that $Av = \mu v$. Any vector u such that $Au = \mu u$ is an eigenvector belonging to the eigenvalue μ. Problem 3.10 shows that the eigenvalues of A are the roots of the *characteristic equation* $|A - \lambda I| = 0$. Even if A is real its eigenvalues (and hence its eigenvectors) may be complex. Consequently we have to be prepared to use complex matrices.

The preceding ideas have applications in the theory of differential equations and we will use the derivative of a general matrix $A = [a_{ij}]$ whose elements are functions of a variable t. This is defined by $dA/dt = [da_{ij}/dt]$ and it is easy to check its properties. In particular we note the product rule

$$\frac{d}{dt}(AB) = A\frac{dB}{dt} + \frac{dA}{dt}B.$$

Problem 4.1 A is a square matrix and T is a non-singular matrix such that $T^{-1}AT = \text{diag}\{\lambda_1, \ldots, \lambda_n\}$. Show that the column vectors of T are eigenvectors of A corresponding to the eigenvalues $\lambda_1, \ldots, \lambda_n$.

Solution. Write $\Lambda = \text{diag}\{\lambda_1, \ldots, \lambda_n\}$ so that $AT = T\Lambda$. Let $v_1, \ldots, v_n$ denote the column vectors of T. Problem 1.22 shows that the column vectors of AT are $Av_1, \ldots, Av_n$ and that those of $T\Lambda$ are $\lambda_1 v_1, \ldots, \lambda_n v_n$. Consequently $Av_i = \lambda_i v_i$, $i = 1, \ldots, n$.

Conversely if A is an $n \times n$ matrix which admits eigenvectors $v_1, \ldots, v_n$ such that $T = [v_1 \ldots v_n]$ is non-singular then $T^{-1}AT$ is diagonal. $\square$

Problem 4.2   Find a matrix T such that $T^{-1}AT$ is diagonal if
(i) $A = \begin{bmatrix} 2 & -3 \\ 1 & -2 \end{bmatrix}$ (ii) $A = \begin{bmatrix} 1 & -1 \\ 1 & 1 \end{bmatrix}$.

Solution. According to Problem 4.1 we must try to construct T from the eigenvectors of A.

(i) The eigenvalues of A are given by $|A - \lambda I| = \lambda^2 - 1 = 0$ and are therefore ± 1. The eigenvectors u corresponding to the eigenvalue $+1$ satisfy $(A - I)u = 0$ or

$$u_1 - 3u_2 = 0, \qquad u_1 - 3u_2 = 0.$$

The general solution is $u_2 = \alpha$, $u_1 = 3\alpha$ or $u = \alpha[3 \ \ 1]'$ where α is arbitrary. Similarly we find that the eigenvectors corresponding to the eigenvalue -1 are $\beta[1 \ \ 1]'$ where β is arbitrary. There is a wide choice for the eigenvectors to make up the non-singular matrix T. We choose $T = \begin{bmatrix} 3 & 1 \\ 1 & 1 \end{bmatrix}$ and check that T is non-singular. Problem 4.1 shows that

$$T^{-1}AT = \begin{bmatrix} 1 & 0 \\ 0 & -1 \end{bmatrix}.$$

(ii) The only difference in this case is that the eigenvalues $1 \pm i$ are complex. Consequently T has to be complex. We construct T from the eigenvectors as $T = \begin{bmatrix} i & -i \\ 1 & 1 \end{bmatrix}$ and then $T^{-1}AT = \mathrm{diag}\{1+i, 1-i\}$ $\qquad \square$

Problem 4.3 (i) Find the general solution of the simultaneous differential equations $dx_1/dt = 2x_1 - 3x_2$, $dx_2/dt = x_1 - 2x_2$.

(ii) Find the solution of the simultaneous differential equations $dx_1/dt = x_1 - x_2$, $dx_2/dt = x_1 + x_2$ such that $x_1(0) = 1$, $x_2(0) = 0$.

Solution. (i) In matrix form the differential equations are $dx/dt = Ax$ where $x = [x_1 \ x_2]'$ and A is the matrix in Problem 4.2(i). We make a linear change of variables $x = Ty$ where T is a constant non-singular matrix and find that

$$dy/dt = T^{-1} dx/dt = T^{-1}ATy.$$

It follows that if we choose T to be the matrix $\begin{bmatrix} 3 & 1 \\ 1 & 1 \end{bmatrix}$ found in Problem 4.2(i) then y_1, y_2 satisfy the differential equations $dy/dt = \begin{bmatrix} 1 & 0 \\ 0 & -1 \end{bmatrix}y$

or $dy_1/dt = y_1$, $dy_2/dt = -y_2$. The general solution of these equations is $y_1 = a e^t$, $y = b e^{-t}$ where a and b are arbitrary constants. The functions x_1, x_2 are given by $x = Ty$ and consequently the required general solution is

$$x_1 = 3a\, e^t + b\, e^{-t}, \qquad x_2 = a\, e^t + b\, e^{-t}.$$

(ii) In matrix form the differential equations are $dx/dt = Ax$ where A is the matrix in Problem 4.2(ii). Using the matrix T in that problem and the transformation $x = Ty$ we find that

$$dy_1/dt = (1+i)y_1, \qquad dy_2/dt = (1-i)y_2.$$

These equations have the complex valued solutions $y_1 = a\,e^{(1+i)t}$, $y_2 = b\,e^{(1-i)t}$ where a and b are arbitrary complex numbers. The solutions to the original differential equations can now be found from $x = Ty$ where we have to choose a,b so that

$$x(0) = \begin{bmatrix} 1 \\ 0 \end{bmatrix} = Ty(0) = \begin{bmatrix} i & -i \\ 1 & 1 \end{bmatrix} \begin{bmatrix} a \\ b \end{bmatrix}.$$

Consequently $a = -b = -\tfrac{1}{2}i$ and, because $e^{(1\pm i)t} = e^t(\cos t \pm i\sin t)$, it follows that $x_1 = e^t \cos t$, $x_2 = e^t \sin t$. $\qquad\square$

Problem 4.4 Find the eigenvalues and eigenvectors of

(i) $A = \begin{bmatrix} -1 & 2 & -3 \\ 0 & 1 & -1 \\ 1 & -1 & 2 \end{bmatrix}$ (ii) $B = \begin{bmatrix} 0 & 1 & -1 \\ 1 & 0 & 1 \\ 1 & -1 & 2 \end{bmatrix}$

Is either matrix similar to a diagonal matrix?

Solution.(i) The characteristic equation is

$$\begin{bmatrix} -1-\lambda & 2 & -3 \\ 0 & 1-\lambda & -1 \\ 1 & -1 & 2-\lambda \end{bmatrix} = 0.$$

A calculation of the determinant, for example by an expansion along the first column, leads to $-\lambda(\lambda-1)^2 = 0$ so that the eigenvalues are 0 and 1. The eigenvectors u corresponding to the eigenvalue 0 satisfy

$$-u_1 + 2u_2 - 3u_3 = 0, \qquad u_2 - u_3 = 0, \qquad u_1 - u_2 + 2u_3 = 0$$

and the solution of these linear equations by the methods of Chapter 3 gives $u_1 = -\alpha$, $u_2 = \alpha$, $u_3 = \alpha$ where α is arbitrary. The eigenvectors u corresponding to the eigenvalue 1 satisfy

$$-2u_1 + 2u_2 - 3u_3 = 0, \qquad -u_3 = 0, \qquad u_1 - u_2 + u_3 = 0$$

and so $u_1 = \beta$, $u_2 = \beta$, $u_3 = 0$ where β is arbitrary.

Any 3×3 matrix whose column vectors are eigenvectors of A is a singular matrix. For at least two columns of such a matrix would be scalar multiples of each other. Consequently Problem 4.1 shows that A is not similar to a diagonal matrix.

(ii) $|B - \lambda I| = -\lambda(\lambda-1)^2$ and so the eigenvalues of B are 0 and 1. The eigenvectors u corresponding to $\lambda = 0$ are given by $u_1 = -\alpha$, $u_2 = \alpha$,

40

$u_3 = \alpha$ where α is arbitrary. The eigenvectors corresponding to $\lambda = 1$ satisfy

$$-u_1 + u_2 - u_3 = 0, \qquad u_1 - u_2 + u_3 = 0, \qquad u_1 - u_2 + u_3 = 0$$

and are therefore given by $u_1 = \beta - \gamma$, $u_2 = \beta$, $u_3 = \gamma$ where β and γ are both arbitrary. In contrast to part (i) a non-singular matrix can be constructed from the eigenvectors. We use the eigenvectors determined by the choices $\alpha = 1$; $\beta = 1$, $\gamma = 0$; $\beta = 0$, $\gamma = 1$ to construct the matrix

$$T = \begin{bmatrix} -1 & 1 & -1 \\ 1 & 1 & 0 \\ 1 & 0 & 1 \end{bmatrix}$$

and $T^{-1}AT = \mathrm{diag}\{0, 1, 1\}$.

There are many types of matrices which are similar to diagonal matrices. For example this is true of any $n \times n$ matrix with n distinct eigenvalues. It is also true of any real symmetric matrix. We note that A and B have the same characteristic equation and that the eigenvalue 1 occurs twice. B is similar to a diagonal matrix but A is not. $\qquad \square$

Problem 4.5 (i) Show that the relation of similarity between matrices is an equivalence relation.

(ii) A,B are real matrices which are similar as complex matrices. Show that they are also similar as real matrices.

Solution. (i) We write $A \sim B$ if $B = T^{-1}AT$ for some non-singular matrix T. This relation is an *equivalence relation* if (a) $A \sim A$ (b) $A \sim B$ implies $B \sim A$ (c) $A \sim B$ and $B \sim C$ implies $A \sim C$. (a) is true because $A = I^{-1}AI$. (b) is true because $B = T^{-1}AT$ implies $A = (T^{-1})^{-1}BT^{-1}$. (c) is true because $B = T^{-1}AT$ and $C = S^{-1}BS$ implies $C = (TS)^{-1}ATS$.

(ii) We are given that there is a non-singular complex matrix T such that $B = T^{-1}AT$ and we have to show that there is a non-singular real matrix S such that $B = S^{-1}AS$. We express $T = X + iY$ where X and Y are real matrices. The relation $TB = AT$ shows that $XB = AX$, $YB = AY$ and consequently $(X + \lambda Y)B = A(X + \lambda Y)$ for any real or complex number λ. The determinant $\phi(\lambda) = |X + \lambda Y|$ is a polynomial in λ with real coefficients. These coefficients are not all zero because $\phi(i) \neq 0$ and therefore there are real values of λ for which $\phi(\lambda) \neq 0$. We may choose $S = X + \mu Y$ where μ is any real number such that $\phi(\mu) \neq 0$. $\qquad \square$

Problem 4.6 Prove that the sum of the eigenvalues of a matrix A is trace A and that their product is $|A|$. Test these relations on the matrix A in Problem 4.4.

Solution. The *trace* of the $n \times n$ matrix A is the sum of its diagonal elements. We consider the *characteristic polynomial* $\phi(\lambda)$ of A defined by

$$\phi(\lambda) = |A - \lambda I| = \begin{vmatrix} a_{11} - \lambda & a_{12} & \cdot & a_{1n} \\ a_{21} & a_{22} - \lambda & \cdot & a_{2n} \\ \cdot & \cdot & \cdot & \cdot \\ a_{n1} & a_{n2} & \cdot & a_{nn} - \lambda \end{vmatrix}$$

The definition (2.1) of a determinant shows that the highest power of λ is n and that this occurs only in the term $(a_{11} - \lambda) \ldots (a_{nn} - \lambda)$. Its coefficient is $(-1)^n$. The power λ^{n-1} also can occur only in this term and its coefficient is therefore $(-1)^{n-1}(a_{11} + \ldots + a_{nn}) = (-1)^{n-1}\text{trace } A$. The constant term in $\phi(\lambda)$ is obtained by substituting $\lambda = 0$ and is therefore $|A|$. Consequently $\phi(\lambda) = (-1)^n(\lambda^n - (\text{trace } A)\lambda^{n-1} + \ldots + (-1)^n|A|)$. On the other hand $\phi(\lambda) = (-1)^n(\lambda - \lambda_1) \ldots (\lambda - \lambda_n)$ where $\lambda_1, \ldots, \lambda_n$ are the eigenvalues of A. We find by comparing the terms in λ^{n-1} and the constant terms that trace $A = \lambda_1 + \ldots + \lambda_n$ and $|A| = \lambda_1 \cdots \lambda_n$.

In Problem 4.4 trace $A = 2$, $|A| = 0$. These agree with the sum $0 + 1 + 1$ and the product $(0)(1)(1)$ of the eigenvalues. $\square$

Problem 4.7 An $n \times n$ matrix $A = [a_{ij}]$ is said to be stochastic if

$$a_{ij} \geqslant 0, \qquad a_{i1} + \ldots + a_{in} = 1, \qquad i, j = 1, \ldots, n.$$

Show that the product of two stochastic matrices is stochastic. Show also that the eigenvalues μ of A satisfy $|\mu| \leqslant 1$.

Solution. If A, B have elements which are $\geqslant 0$ then so has AB. In terms of $l = [11 \ldots 1]'$ the second condition is $Al = $ If A, B satisfy this condition then so does AB because $(AB)l = A(Bl) = Al = l$.

Choose a non-zero eigenvector $v = [v_1 \ldots v_n]'$ corresponding to the eigenvalue μ. Let v_α be an element of v with the largest absolute value. Because $Av = \mu v$ we have, in particular, $a_{\alpha 1} v_1 + \ldots + a_{\alpha n} v_n = \mu v_\alpha$. Using the modulus inequality and the conditions on a stochastic matrix we find

$$|\mu| = \left| a_{\alpha 1} \frac{v_1}{v_\alpha} + \ldots + a_{\alpha n} \frac{v_n}{v_\alpha} \right| \leqslant a_{\alpha 1} \left| \frac{v_1}{v_\alpha} \right| + \ldots + a_{\alpha n} \left| \frac{v_n}{v_\alpha} \right| \leqslant a_{\alpha 1} + \ldots + a_{\alpha n} = 1.$$

$\square$

4.2 Orthogonal and Unitary Matrices The *scalar product* $\langle x, y \rangle$ of two real column vectors is defined by $\langle x, y \rangle = x_1 y_1 + \ldots + x_n y_n$.

We can write this as $x'y$ where, as usual, we do not distinguish between a 1×1 matrix and its element. x and y are *orthogonal* if $\langle x, y \rangle = 0$ and the *norm* or length of x is $\langle x, x \rangle^{\frac{1}{2}}$.

We extend the scalar product to complex vectors by $\langle x, y \rangle = x'\bar{y} = x_1 \bar{y}_1 + \ldots + x_n \bar{y}_n$. Notice that the extended product is not symmetric but $\langle y, x \rangle = \overline{\langle x, y \rangle}$. The previous definitions of orthogonality and norm apply to the complex case.

An orthogonal matrix is a real square matrix T such that $T'T = I$. Consequently it is non-singular and the inverse is the transpose. If T is partitioned into its column vectors $v_1, \ldots, v_n$ and T' into its row vectors $v'_1, \ldots, v'_n$ then $T'T = [v'_i v_j]$. Therefore T is orthogonal if and only if $v'_i v_j = \delta_{ij}$ that is, if and only if its column vectors are of unit norm and mutually orthogonal. Orthogonal matrices are important in euclidean geometry.

In complex matrices the idea of an orthogonal matrix generalizes to that of a unitary matrix. This is a square matrix U such that $\bar{U}'U = I$. U is unitary if and only if its column vectors are of unit norm and mutually orthogonal. A real unitary matrix is orthogonal.

Problem 4.8 (i) Show that A is orthogonal and that U is unitary where

$$A = \frac{1}{3}\begin{bmatrix} 1 & -2 & 2 \\ 2 & -1 & -2 \\ 2 & 2 & 1 \end{bmatrix}, \quad U = \frac{1}{\sqrt{3}}\begin{bmatrix} 1+i & 1 \\ i & -1-i \end{bmatrix}.$$

(ii) Show that any 2×2 orthogonal matrix is either

$$\begin{bmatrix} \cos\theta & -\sin\theta \\ \sin\theta & \cos\theta \end{bmatrix} \quad \text{or} \quad \begin{bmatrix} \cos\theta & \sin\theta \\ \sin\theta & -\cos\theta \end{bmatrix}$$

for some angle θ.

Solution. (i) The first two columns of A are orthogonal because $(1)(-2)+(2)(-1)+(2)(2) = 0$. The norm of the first column is $\frac{1}{3}(1+4+4)^{\frac{1}{2}} = 1$. Further calculations of this kind show that A is orthogonal.

The norm of the first column of U is $3^{-\frac{1}{2}}((1+i)(1-i)+i(-i))^{\frac{1}{2}} = 1$. The second column also has norm 1. The columns are orthogonal because $(1+i)(1)+(i)(-1+i) = 0$.

(ii) If $\begin{bmatrix} a & b \\ c & d \end{bmatrix}$ is orthogonal then $a^2+c^2 = b^2+d^2 = 1$, $ab+cd = 0$.

There are angles $\theta, \phi (0 \leqslant \theta, \phi < 2\pi)$ such that $a = \cos\theta$, $c = \sin\theta$, $b = \sin\phi$, $d = \cos\phi$. θ and ϕ are related by $\sin(\theta+\phi) = 0$ so that

43

$\theta + \phi$ is one of the angles $0, \pi, 2\pi, 3\pi$. It follows that either $\sin \phi = -\sin \theta$, $\cos \phi = \cos \theta$ or $\sin \phi = \sin \theta$, $\cos \phi = -\cos \theta$. $\qquad\square$

Problem 4.9 (i) Prove that the determinant of a unitary matrix has modulus 1.

(ii) A, B are unitary matrices of the same order. Prove that AB and A^{-1} are also unitary matrices.

Solution. (i) We know that $|\bar{A}'| = \overline{|A|}$. Consequently if A is unitary
$$\overline{|A|}\,|A| = |\bar{A}'|\,|A| = |\bar{A}'A| = |I| = 1$$
and so the modulus of the complex number $|A|$ is 1. Note that if A is orthogonal then $|A|$ is real and therefore $|A| = \pm 1$.

(ii) AB is unitary because $(\overline{AB})'AB = \bar{B}'\bar{A}'AB = \bar{B}'B = I$. To prove that A^{-1} is unitary we put $U = A^{-1}$ so that $\bar{U} = (\overline{A^{-1}}) = \bar{A}^{-1}$. Then $\bar{U}'U = \bar{U}'A^{-1} = \bar{U}'\bar{A}' = (\bar{A}U)' = I' = I$. $\qquad\square$

Problem 4.10 Prove that the eigenvalues of a unitary matrix have modulus 1. Test this fact on the 2×2 orthogonal matrices.

Solution. Let μ be an eigenvalue of the $n \times n$ unitary matrix U and choose a corresponding non-zero eigenvector x. We transpose and conjugate the relation $Ux = \mu x$ to obtain $\bar{x}'\bar{U}' = \bar{\mu}\bar{x}'$. Consequently $\bar{\mu}\mu\bar{x}'x = \bar{x}'\bar{U}'Ux = \bar{x}'x$ and, as $\bar{x}'x = \bar{x}_1 x_1 + \ldots + \bar{x}_n x_n$ is a non-zero number, it follows that $\bar{\mu}\mu = 1$.

The two kinds of 2×2 orthogonal matrices occur in Problem 4.8(ii). Their eigenvalues are $e^{\pm i\theta}$ and ± 1 respectively. $\qquad\square$

Problem 4.11 (i) Prove that the eigenvalues of a hermitian matrix are real and that eigenvectors belonging to distinct eigenvalues are orthogonal.

(ii) Prove that the eigenvalues of a skew-hermitian matrix are purely imaginary.

Solution. (i) Let μ be an eigenvalue of the hermitian matrix A and choose a corresponding non-zero eigenvector x. We multiply the relation $Ax = \mu x$ by $\bar{x}'$ to obtain $\bar{x}'Ax = \mu\bar{x}'x$. $\bar{x}'x$ is a real positive number and therefore Problem 1.31 shows that $\mu = \bar{x}'Ax/\bar{x}'x$ is a real number.

Let x, y be eigenvectors belonging to the distinct eigenvalues μ, ν. Because μ is real the conjugate of the relation $Ax = \mu x$ is $\bar{A}\bar{x} = \mu\bar{x}$. We multiply by y' to obtain $y'\bar{A}\bar{x} = \mu y'\bar{x}$. On the other hand the transpose of $Ay = \nu y$ is $y'A' = \nu y'$ and we multiply by $\bar{x}$ to obtain $y'A'\bar{x} = \nu y'\bar{x}$. As A is hermitian $A' = \bar{A}$ and consequently $\nu y'\bar{x} = \mu y'\bar{x}$. But $\nu \neq \mu$ and therefore $y'\bar{x} = 0$.

(ii) Exactly as in part (i) $\mu = \bar{x}'Ax/\bar{x}'x$ where x is a non-zero eigenvector belonging to the eigenvalue μ. Because A is skew-hermitian Problem 1.31 shows that μ is purely imaginary.

We note that this problem applies in particular to real symmetric and skew-symmetric matrices. $\qquad\square$

Problem 4.12 (Cayley's construction) If S is a real skew-symmetric matrix show that $I+S$ is non-singular and that $(I+S)^{-1}(I-S)$ is an orthogonal matrix with determinant $+1$.

Use this construction to obtain an orthogonal matrix from
$$\begin{bmatrix} 0 & \tan\tfrac{1}{2}\theta \\ -\tan\tfrac{1}{2}\theta & 0 \end{bmatrix}.$$

Solution. Problem 4.11(ii) shows that S cannot have an eigenvalue -1 and therefore $|I+S| \neq 0$. We put $U = (I+S)^{-1}(I-S)$. Then, using Problem 1.24,

$$UU' = (I+S)^{-1}(I-S)(I-S)'((I+S)')^{-1} =$$
$$= (I+S)^{-1}(I-S)(I+S)(I-S)^{-1}$$
$$= (I+S)^{-1}(I+S)(I-S)(I-S)^{-1} = I$$

because $(I-S)(I+S) = I-S^2 = (I+S)(I-S)$. Therefore U is orthogonal. Further, using Problem 2.4 we find that $|I-S| = |I-S'| = |I+S|$. Because $(I+S)U = I-S$ and consequently $|I+S||U| = |I-S|$ it follows that $|U| = 1$.

A calculation shows that if

$$S = \begin{bmatrix} 0 & \tan\tfrac{1}{2}\theta \\ -\tan\tfrac{1}{2}\theta & 0 \end{bmatrix}$$

then
$$(I+S)^{-1}(I-S) = \begin{bmatrix} \cos\theta & -\sin\theta \\ \sin\theta & \cos\theta \end{bmatrix}.$$

Problem 4.13 (x_1, x_2, x_3) are rectangular cartesian coordinates in euclidean space and (y_1, y_2, y_3) is another such system with the same origin. Prove that $x = Ty$ where $x = [x_1\ x_2\ x_3]'$, $y = [y_1\ y_2\ y_3]'$ and T is an orthogonal matrix.

Solution. Let O be the origin of the x-coordinate system and let $\mathbf{a}_1, \mathbf{a}_2, \mathbf{a}_3$ be unit vectors along the coordinate axes. Let $\mathbf{b}_1, \mathbf{b}_2, \mathbf{b}_3$ be unit vectors along the y-coordinate axes. Then

$$\mathbf{b}_i = t_{1i}\mathbf{a}_1 + t_{2i}\mathbf{a}_2 + t_{3i}\mathbf{a}_3, \qquad i = 1, 2, 3 \qquad (4.1)$$

where t_{1i}, t_{2i}, t_{3i} are the components of the vector $\mathbf{b}_i$ with respect to the x-coordinate system. The scalar product $\mathbf{b}_i \cdot \mathbf{b}_j = \delta_{ij}$ and therefore

$t_{1i}t_{1j}+t_{2i}t_{2j}+t_{3i}t_{3j} = \delta_{ij}$. Consequently the matrix $T = [t_{ij}]$ is orthogonal.

The coordinates of a general point P with respect to the two systems are related by

$$\mathbf{OP} = x_1\,\mathbf{a}_1+x_2\,\mathbf{a}_2+x_3\,\mathbf{a}_3 = y_1\,\mathbf{b}_1+y_2\,\mathbf{b}_2+y_3\,\mathbf{b}_3\,.$$

We substitute for $\mathbf{b}_1,\mathbf{b}_2.\,\mathbf{b}_3$ from equation (4.1) and obtain $x_j = t_{j1}\,y_1+t_{j2}\,y_2+t_{j3}\,y_3$ or, in matrix form, $x = Ty$.

Conversely given the x-coordinate system and any 3×3 orthogonal matrix the equation $x = Ty$ defines a rectangular cartesian coordinate system (y_1,y_2,y_3) $\qquad\qquad\square$

Problem 4.14 (i) Show that a 3×3 orthogonal matrix A with $|A| = 1$ has an eigenvalue 1.

(ii) Prove that any direct isometry of euclidean space which has a fixed point is a rotation about an axis.

Solution. (i) The 3 eigenvalues of the real matrix A are either all real or one is real and the others are complex conjugates. They are of modulus 1 (Problem 4.10) and their product is 1 (Problem 4.6). These facts imply that at least one eigenvalue is 1.

(ii) An *isometry* (or rigid motion) is a transformation of euclidean space which does not alter distances between points. Let (x_1,x_2,x_3), (y_1,y_2,y_3) be respectively the rectangular cartesian coordinates of a point P and of the point to which P moves under the isometry. Put $x[x_1\,x_2\,x_3]'$ and $y = [y_1\,y_2\,y_3]'$. Then it can be proved that $y = Ax+a$ where A is orthogonal and a is a column vector. The isometry is direct if $|A| = 1$.

We choose coordinates with origin the fixed point of the given isometry. Thus $y = Ax$ with A orthogonal and $|A| = 1$. A has an eigenvalue 1 (part (i)) and so there is a non-zero vector v such that $Av = v$. Since $A(\alpha v) = \alpha v$ for any α, there is a line of fixed points of coordinates αv. Choose a new system of coordinates with the same origin but with the third coordinate axis along this line. In this new system $y = Bx$ where the third column of B is $[0\ 0\ 1]'$. Because the columns of B are mutually orthogonal $B =$

$$\begin{bmatrix} & & 0 \\ & C & 0 \\ 0 & 0 & 1 \end{bmatrix}.$$

Because B is orthogonal with $|B| = 1$, C is orthogonal and $|C| = 1$. Therefore (Problem 4.8) $C = \begin{bmatrix} \cos\theta & -\sin\theta \\ \sin\theta & \cos\theta \end{bmatrix}$ for some angle θ.

It is now a matter of easy coordinate geometry to show that $y = Bx$ represents a rotation through an angle θ about the third coordinate axis. $\qquad\square$

4.3 Orthogonal Transformations of Real Quadratic Forms

Under a change of variables $x = Ty$ a real quadratic form $x'Ax$ is expressed as a quadratic form $y'T'ATy$ in the variables $y_1,\ldots,y_n$ (see § 1.6). The problem of finding an orthogonal matrix T such that $y'T'ATy$ is a diagonal form $\lambda_1 y_1^2 +\ldots+\lambda_n y_n^2$ arises in several of the applications of matrix theory. If T is orthogonal then $T' = T^{-1}$ and the problem can be expressed in terms of matrices as follows. Given a real symmetric $n\times n$ matrix A find an orthogonal matrix T such that $T^{-1}AT$ is diagonal. We use the methods of § 4.1.

The construction of T is easily seen to be possible when A has distinct eigenvalues. For these are real (Problem 4.11) and we can therefore choose n corresponding real eigenvectors of norm 1. These eigenvectors are orthogonal to each other (Problem 4.11) and therefore form the columns of an orthogonal matrix T such that $T^{-1}AT$ is diagonal. In fact the construction of T is always possible. Thus if an eigenvalue λ of A is repeated r times it is always possible to choose r eigenvectors belonging to λ which are of norm 1 and mutually orthogonal.

Problem 4.15 Construct an orthogonal matrix T such that $T^{-1}AT$ is diagonal if

(i) $A = \begin{bmatrix} 7 & 2 & 0 \\ 2 & 6 & 2 \\ 0 & 2 & 5 \end{bmatrix}$ (ii) $A = \begin{bmatrix} 8 & -3 & -3 \\ -3 & 8 & -3 \\ -3 & -3 & 8 \end{bmatrix}$.

Solution. (i) A calculation gives $|A - \lambda I| = -\lambda^3 + 18\lambda^2 - 99\lambda + 162 = -(\lambda-3)(\lambda-6)(\lambda-9)$ and so A has the distinct eigenvalues $3, 6, 9$. The general eigenvector u belonging to the eigenvalue 3 is found by solving $(A-3I)u = 0$. We find $u = \alpha[\tfrac{1}{2} \quad -1 \quad 1]'$. The square of norm u is $9\alpha^2/4$ and we put $\alpha = \tfrac{2}{3}$ to obtain an eigenvector of norm 1.

We construct in the same way eigenvectors of norm 1 belonging to the eigenvalues 6 and 9. The three vectors form the columns of the orthogonal matrix

$$T = \tfrac{1}{3}\begin{bmatrix} 1 & -2 & 2 \\ -2 & 1 & 2 \\ 2 & 2 & 1 \end{bmatrix}$$

and $T^{-1}AT = \mathrm{diag}\{3, 6.9\}$.

(ii) The elementary operations (col. 2) − (col. 1), (col. 3) − (col. 1) carried out on $A - \lambda I$ lead to $|A - \lambda I| = (11 - \lambda)^2(2 - \lambda)$. Therefore we must choose two eigenvectors belonging to the eigenvalue 11 which are mutually orthogonal and of norm 1. The general solution of $(A - 11I)u = 0$ is $u = [-(\alpha - \beta) \quad \beta \quad \alpha]'$ where α, β are arbitrary. Choose $\beta = 0$, $\alpha = 1/\sqrt{2}$ to give an eigenvector $v = (1/\sqrt{2})[-1 \quad 0 \quad 1]'$ of norm 1. Now choose α, β so that u is orthogonal to v and of norm 1. The orthogonality condition is $\alpha + \beta + \alpha = 0$ and so we choose $\alpha = 1/\sqrt{6}$, $\beta = -2/\sqrt{6}$.

Finally we obtain an eigenvector of norm 1 belonging to the eigenvalue 2. The three vectors form the columns of the orthogonal matrix

$$T = \frac{1}{\sqrt{6}} \begin{bmatrix} \sqrt{2} & -\sqrt{3} & 1 \\ \sqrt{2} & 0 & -2 \\ \sqrt{2} & \sqrt{3} & 1 \end{bmatrix}$$

and $T^{-1}AT = \text{diag}\{2, 11, 11\}$. Note the infinity of possible choices for the columns of T corresponding to the repeated eigenvalue 11. ☐

Problem 4.16 (x_1, x_2, x_3) are rectangular cartesian coordinates in space. Find the lengths and directions of the principal axes of the central quadrics whose equations are

(i) $7x_1^2 + 6x_2^2 + 5x_3^2 + 4x_1 x_2 + 4x_2 x_3 = 1$
(ii) $8(x_1^2 + x_2^2 + x_3^2) - 6(x_2 x_3 + x_3 x_1 + x_1 x_2) = 1.$

Solution. If the equation of a quadric with respect to rectangular cartesian coordinates (y_1, y_2, y_3) is $\lambda_1 y_1^2 + \lambda_2 y_2^2 + \lambda_3 y_3^2 = 1$ then the coordinate axes are *principal axes* of the quadric. If $\lambda_1, \lambda_2, \lambda_3$ are all > 0 then the quadric is an *ellipsoid* and $1/\sqrt{\lambda_1}, 1/\sqrt{\lambda_2}, 1/\sqrt{\lambda_3}$ are the *lengths* of the principal axes.

(i) We use the matrices A, T occurring in Problem 4.15(i). The quadric has equation $x'Ax = 1$. In terms of new coordinates defined by $x = Ty$ this becomes $3y_1^2 + 6y_2^2 + 9y_3^2 = 1$ and so the new coordinate axes are principal axes. The columns of T give the components of unit vectors along the principal axes (Problem 4.13). The quadric is an ellipsoid and the lengths of its principal axes are $1/\sqrt{3}, 1/\sqrt{6}, 1/3$.

(ii) The solution can be read off from the solution to Problem 4.15(ii). In particular the equation of the quadric referred to principal axes is $2y_1^2 + 11(y_2^2 + y_3^2) = 1$. But because A has a repeated eigenvalue the principal axes are not uniquely determined. The quadric is formed by rotating an ellipse about the y_1 axis.

Note that for any quadric of equation $x'Ax = 1$ the directions (lengths) of the principal axes are determined by the eigenvectors (eigenvalues) of A. □

4.4 Matrix Polynomials

Given a polynomial function $f(\lambda) = a_0 \lambda^m + \ldots + a_{m-1} \lambda + a_m$ of a complex variable λ we define a corresponding matrix polynomial $f(X) = a_0 X^m + \ldots a_{m-1} X + a_m I$ where X is any complex square matrix. Note that in the matrix case the constant term is $a_m I$. There are some important polynomials associated with a given square matrix A. We have already met the characteristic polynomial $\phi(\lambda) = |A - \lambda I|$. The Cayley-Hamilton Theorem states that $\phi(A) = 0$. A minimum polynomial of A is a polynomial ψ of lowest degree such that $\psi(A) = 0$. ψ is necessarily a factor of ϕ.

Problem 4.17 Given $f(X) = X^3 + X + I$ and $g(X) = X^2 + 3x + 2I$
(i) express f as $qg + r$ where q, r are matrix polynomials and degree $r < 2$.
(ii) factorize the matrix polynomial g.

Solution. (i) $X^3 + X + I = X(X^2 + 3X + 2I) - 3X^2 - X + I$

$$= X(X^2 + 3X + 2I) - 3(X^2 + 3X + 2I)$$
$$+ 8X + 5I$$
$$= (X - 3I)(X^2 + 3X + 2I) + 8X + 5I$$

and so $q(X) = X - 3I, r(X) = 8X + 5I$.

(ii) $g(X) = X^2 + 3X + 2I = (X + 2I)(X + I)$. □

Problem 4.18 Let f denote a polynomial. Prove that

(i) if $\Lambda = \text{diag}\{\lambda_1, \ldots, \lambda_n\}$ then $f(\Lambda) = \text{diag}\{f(\lambda_1), \ldots, f(\lambda_n)\}$
(ii) $f(T^{-1}AT) = T^{-1}f(A)T$
(iii) if μ is an eigenvalue of A then $f(\mu)$ is an eigenvalue of $f(A)$. In particular $f(A) = O$ implies $f(\mu) = 0$.

Solution. We put

$$f(X) = a_0 X^m + \ldots + a_{m-1} X + a_m I. \tag{4.2}$$

(i) For any integer r, $\Lambda^r = \text{diag}\{\lambda_1^r, \ldots, \lambda_n^r\}$. We substitute in the definition (4.2) and obtain $f(\Lambda) = \text{diag}\{f(\lambda_1), \ldots, f(\lambda_n)\}$.

(ii) Put $X = T^{-1}AT$. Then $X^2 = (T^{-1}AT)(T^{-1}AT) = T^{-1}A^2T$ and in general, $X^r = T^{-1}A^rT$ for any integer r. We substitute in the definition (4.2) and obtain $f(X) = T^{-1}f(A)T$.

(iii) Let μ be an eigenvalue of A and x a corresponding eigenvector. Then $A^2x = A(Ax) = A(\mu x) = \mu(Ax) = \mu^2 x$ and in general, $A^r x = \mu^r x$ for any integer r. It follows from the definition (4.2) that $f(A)x =$

$f(\mu)x$ so that $f(\mu)$ is an eigenvalue of $f(A)$. If $f(A) = O$ then $f(\mu)$ is an eigenvalue of a zero matrix and hence $f(\mu) = 0$. $\qquad\square$

Problem 4.19 Let ψ be a minimum polynomial of a square matrix A. Show that if f is any polynomial such that $f(A) = O$ then $f = q\psi$ for some polynomial q.

Solution. The division algorithm for polynomials (see Problem 4.17(i) for an example of this algorithm) shows that $f = q\psi + r$ where either (a) r is the zero polynomial or (b) r is a non-zero polynomial and degree r < degree ψ. Because $f(A) = O$ and $\psi(A) = O$ it follows that $r(A) = O$. Consequently the fact that ψ is a minimum polynomial rules out (b), and $f = q\psi$.

This problem shows that any two minimum polynomials of A are scalar multiples of each other. Together with the Cayley–Hamilton Theorem it shows that a minimum polynomial of A is a factor of the characteristic polynomial of A. $\qquad\square$

Problem 4.20 Prove that similar matrices have the same characteristic and minimum polynomials.

Solution. Let A, B be similar so that $B = T^{-1}AT$. Then $B - \lambda I = T^{-1}(A - \lambda I)T$ and therefore $|B - \lambda I| = |T^{-1}||A - \lambda I||T| = |A - \lambda I|$. A consequence of this fact is that if A is similar to a diagonal matrix Λ then the diagonal elements of Λ are the eigenvalues of A, each repeated according to its multiplicity as a root of the characteristic polynomial of A.

Let f, g be minimum polynomials of A, B respectively. From Problem 4.18(ii) $f(B) = T^{-1}f(A)T = O$ and $g(A) = T g(B)T^{-1} = O$. It follows from Problem 4.19 that g is a factor of f and that f is a factor of g. Consequently f and g are scalar multiples of each other and are therefore minimum polynomials of both A and B. $\qquad\square$

Problem 4.21 (i) Verify the Cayley–Hamilton Theorem for $A = \begin{bmatrix} 2 & 1 \\ 1 & 2 \end{bmatrix}$ and use it to calculate A^4 and A^{-1}.

(ii) Prove the Cayley–Hamilton Theorem for a matrix similar to a diagonal matrix.

Solution. (i) The characteristic polynomial of A is $\lambda^2 - 4\lambda + 3$. A calculation gives

$$A^2 - 4A + 3I = \begin{bmatrix} 5 & 4 \\ 4 & 5 \end{bmatrix} - 4\begin{bmatrix} 2 & 1 \\ 1 & 2 \end{bmatrix} + 3\begin{bmatrix} 1 & 0 \\ 0 & 1 \end{bmatrix} = \begin{bmatrix} 0 & 0 \\ 0 & 0 \end{bmatrix}.$$

Because $A^2 = 4A - 3I$,

50

$$A^3 = A(4A - 3I) = 4A^2 - 3A = 4(4A - 3I) - 3A = 13A - 12I$$

and therefore

$$A^4 = A(13A - 12I) = 13A^2 - 12A = 40A - 39I = \begin{bmatrix} 41 & 40 \\ 40 & 41 \end{bmatrix}.$$

Because $A^2 - 4A + 3I = O$ we obtain from multiplication by A^{-1},

$$A^{-1} = \tfrac{1}{3}(4I - A) = \tfrac{1}{3}\begin{bmatrix} 2 & -1 \\ -1 & 2 \end{bmatrix}.$$

(ii) Suppose A is similar to a diagonal matrix so that, for some T, $T^{-1}AT = \Lambda = \text{diag}\{\lambda_1, \ldots, \lambda_n\}$ where $\lambda_1, \ldots, \lambda_n$ are the eigenvalues of A. Let ϕ be the characteristic polynomial of A. From Problem 4.18 (ii), (i), $\phi(A) = \phi(T\Lambda T^{-1}) = T\phi(\Lambda)T^{-1} = O$ because $\phi(\Lambda) = \text{diag}\{\phi(\lambda_1), \ldots, \phi(\lambda_n)\} = O$.

Problem 4.22   Find a minimum polynomial of

$$A = \begin{bmatrix} -2 & 1 & 1 \\ 1 & -2 & 1 \\ 1 & 1 & -2 \end{bmatrix}.$$

Solution. Our aim is to test the factors of the characteristic polynomial $\phi(\lambda) = |A - \lambda I| = -\lambda(\lambda + 3)^2$ for the minimum polynomial of A. However in this particular case A is symmetric and therefore similar to $\Lambda = \text{diag}\{0, -3, -3\}$. As A has the same characteristic and minimum polynomials as Λ (Problem 4.20) it is sufficient (and easier) to test the factors of ϕ for the minimum polynomial of Λ. We substitute Λ into the linear factors and get the matrices Λ, $\Lambda + 3I = \text{diag}\{3, 0, 0\}$. These are $\neq O$ but their product $\Lambda(\Lambda + 3I) = O$. Consequently $\lambda(\lambda + 3)$ is a minimum polynomial of Λ and hence of A.

The argument can be generalized to show that if A is any matrix similar to a diagonal matrix then $(\lambda - \lambda_1) \ldots (\lambda - \lambda_k)$ is a minimum polynomial of A where $\lambda_1, \ldots, \lambda_k$ are all the distinct eigenvalues of A. The converse statement is also true. That is, if a minimum polynomial of A can be factorized into distinct linear factors then A is similar to a diagonal matrix. $\square$

Problem 4.23 X is a real matrix such that $X^2 = -I$. Prove that, for some n, $X = T^{-1}\begin{bmatrix} O & -I_n \\ I_n & O \end{bmatrix} T$ where T is a real non-singular matrix and I_n is the $n \times n$ unit matrix.

Solution. Because $X^2 + I = O$ a minimum polynomial of X is a factor of $\lambda^2 + 1$ and must therefore factorize into distinct linear complex factors. Consequently X, considered as a complex matrix, is similar to a diagonal matrix. The eigenvalues of X are $\pm i$ (Problem 4.18(iii)) and, because X is real, they occur with the same multiplicity. We denote this multiplicity by n so that X is similar to $\begin{bmatrix} iI_n & O \\ O & -iI_n \end{bmatrix}$.

The matrix $J = \begin{bmatrix} O & -I_n \\ I_n & O \end{bmatrix}$ is real and $J^2 = -I$. Hence J is similar to $\begin{bmatrix} iI_n & O \\ O & -iI_r \end{bmatrix}$ and therefore (Problem 4.5(i)) J is similar to X. The solution follows from Problem 4.5(ii). □

Problem 4.24 Use the exponential function to solve the simultaneous differential equations

$$dx_1/dt = -2x_1 + x_2 + x_3, \qquad dx_2/dt = x_1 - 2x_2 + x_3,$$
$$dx_3/dt = x_1 + x_2 - 2x_3.$$

with the initial conditions $x_1(0) = 0$, $x_2(0) = 3$, $x_3(0) = 0$.

Solution. The exponential series $I + X + X^2/2! + X^3/3! + \ldots$ can be proved convergent for any square matrix X and its sum is denoted by $\exp X$. Further, if t is a real variable and A is constant the derivative of $\exp tA$ is the matrix product $A \exp tA$.

In matrix form the differential equations are $dx/dt = Ax$ where A is the matrix in Problem 4.22. We can verify that the solution with initial conditions $x(0) = [0 \ 3 \ 0]'$ is $(\exp tA) x(0) = (\exp tA) [0 \ 3 \ 0]'$. The function $\exp tA$ can be calculated using the relation $A^2 = -3A$ obtained in Problem 4.22. We find $A^3 = -3A^2 = (-3)^2 A$ and in general $A^n = (-3)^{n-1} A$. Consequently

$$\exp tA = I + tA + \frac{1}{2!}t^2A^2 + \frac{1}{3!}t^3A^3 + \ldots$$

$$= I + \left(t + \frac{1}{2!}t^2(-3) + \frac{1}{3!}t^3(-3)^2 + \ldots \right) A = I + \frac{1}{3}(1 - e^{-3t})A.$$

It follows that the solution is $(I + \frac{1}{3}(1 - e^{-3t})A)[0 \ 3 \ 0]'$ and a calculation gives $x_1 = 1 - e^{-3t}$, $x_2 = 1 + 2e^{-3t}$, $x_3 = 1 - e^{-3t}$.

This method should be compared with the method in Problem 4.3. □

EXERCISES

1. Find a non-singular matrix T such that $T^{-1}AT$ is a diagonal matrix where

$$A = \begin{bmatrix} 0 & 1 & 1 \\ 1 & 0 & 1 \\ 1 & -1 & 0 \end{bmatrix}.$$

Solve the differential equations $dx/dt = Ax$ with the initial conditions $x_1(0) = 0$, $x_2(0) = 1$, $x_3(0) = 0$.

2. (*Gerschgorin's Theorem*) μ is an eigenvalue of the $n \times n$ matrix $[a_{ij}]$. Use an argument in Problem 4.7 to prove that, for some integer α, $1 \leqslant \alpha \leqslant n$,

$$|a_{\alpha\alpha} - \mu| \leqslant \sum_{i \neq \alpha} |a_{\alpha i}|.$$

Show that for the matrix

$$\begin{bmatrix} 0 & 2 & 0 \\ -2 & 4 & 1 \\ 0 & -1 & 0 \end{bmatrix}$$

the inequalities are $|\mu| \leqslant 2$, $|\mu - 4| \leqslant 3$, $|\mu| \leqslant 1$ and test them by calculating the eigenvalues.

3. (i) If A is hermitian then eigenvectors of A belonging to distinct eigenvalues are mutually orthogonal (Problem 4.11). Prove that this is also true if A is skew-hermitian or unitary.

(ii) If S is skew-hermitian show that Cayley's construction (Problem 4.12) gives a unitary matrix.

4. Find an orthogonal matrix T such that $T'AT$ is a diagonal matrix where

$$\text{(i) } A = \begin{bmatrix} 0 & 1 & 0 \\ 1 & 0 & 0 \\ 0 & 0 & 2 \end{bmatrix} \qquad \text{(ii) } A = \begin{bmatrix} 7 & 16 & -8 \\ 16 & 7 & -8 \\ -8 & -8 & -5 \end{bmatrix}.$$

5. (i) Use the Cayley–Hamilton Theorem to show that $A^{-1} = 6A - A^2$, and hence calculate A^{-1}, where

$$A = \begin{bmatrix} 1 & 1 & 1 \\ 2 & 1 & 2 \\ 3 & 2 & 4 \end{bmatrix}.$$

(ii) Find a minimum polynomial of the matrix B in Problem 4.4. Hence show that $\exp tB = I - B + e^t B$ where t is a real variable.

6. (i) Prove that any matrix X such that $X^2 = X$ is either a zero

53

matrix or is similar to $\begin{bmatrix} I_r & O \\ O & O \end{bmatrix}$ for some integer r.

(ii) Prove that any 3×3 real matrix X such that $X^3 = I$ is either a unit matrix or is similar to

$$\begin{bmatrix} 0 & 1 & 0 \\ 0 & 0 & 1 \\ 1 & 0 & 0 \end{bmatrix}.$$

Chapter 5

Real Quadratic Forms

5.1 The Rank and Index of a Real Quadratic Form   A real quadratic form $x'Ax$ in n variables $x_1,\ldots,x_n$ can be reduced by a real non-singular transformation $x = Ty$ to the *normal form* $-y_1^2 - \ldots - y_p^2 + y_{p+1}^2 + \ldots + y_r^2$. Although the reduction can be done in many ways it can be shown that the numbers p, r are always the same. r is the *rank* of the quadratic form and is equal to the rank of A (Problem 5.2(i)). p is the *index* of the quadratic form. A related number is the *signature* which is the difference between the numbers of positive and negative squares in the normal form.

A real quadratic form $x'Ax$ is *positive (negative) definite* if $x'Ax > 0 (< 0)$ for all non-zero values of the vector x. Conditions for a form to be positive or negative definite can be given in terms of the rank and index (Problem 5.4 (i)).

Problem 5.1   (i) Find non-singular linear transformations which reduce the following quadratic forms to normal form:

(a) $2x_1^2 + x_2^2 + x_3^2 + 4x_1x_2 + 2x_1x_3$ (b) $x_1x_2 + x_2x_3 + x_3x_1$
(c) $x_1^2 + 2x_2^2 + x_3^2 + 2x_1x_2 - 2x_2x_3$.

(ii) Find a second reduction of the quadratic form (a) and verify that the numbers p, r are unaltered.

Solution. (i) (a) We first complete the square in the terms involving x_1 and therefore express the form as

$$2(x_1 + x_2 + \tfrac{1}{2}x_3)^2 - x_2^2 + \tfrac{1}{2}x_3^2 - 2x_2x_3.$$

We continue by completing the square in the remaining terms containing x_2. We obtain

$$2(x_1 + x_2 + \tfrac{1}{2}x_3)^2 - (x_2 + x_3)^2 + \tfrac{3}{2}x_3^2.$$

Consequently the non-singular transformation $y_1 = x_2 + x_3$, $y_2 = \sqrt{\tfrac{3}{2}}x_3$, $y_3 = \sqrt{2}(x_1 + x_2 + \tfrac{1}{2}x_3)$ reduces the quadratic form to $-y_1^2 + y_2^2 + y_3^2$.

(b) In this case there are no squared terms and we have first to introduce some. We make the non-singular transformation $x_1 = w_1 + w_2$, $x_2 = w_1 - w_2$, $x_3 = w_3$ so that the form becomes $w_1^2 - w_2^2 + 2w_1w_3$. We can now complete the square as for (a) to obtain

55

$(w_1+w_3)^2-w_2^2-w_3^2$. Finally the transformation $y_1 = w_2$, $y_2 = w_3$, $y_3 = w_1+w_3$ reduces the form to $-y_1^2-y_2^2+y_3^2$.

(c) We complete the square twice to obtain $(x_1+x_2)^2+(x_2-x_3)^2$. The non-singular transformation $y_1 = x_1+x_2$, $y_2 = x_2-x_3$, $y_3 = x_3$ reduces the form to $y_1^2+y_2^2$.

(ii) We obtain a second reduction by completing the square first in the terms containing x_3 and then in the remaining terms containing x_1. The form is expressed as $(x_3+x_1)^2+(x_1+2x_2)^2-3x_2^2$ and the non-singular transformation $w_1 = x_2\sqrt{3}$, $w_2 = x_3+x_1$, $w_3 = x_1+2x_2$ reduces it to $-w_1^2+w_2^2+w_3^2$. Consequently, as in the first reduction, $p = 1, r = 3$. $\qquad\square$

Problem 5.2 (i) Prove that in any reduction of $x'Ax$ to normal form the number of squares is the rank of A.

(ii) Prove that the rank of $x'Ax$ is the number of non-zero eigenvalues of A and that the index is the number of negative eigenvalues.

Solution. (i) Suppose that $x = Ty$ reduces $x'Ax$ to $-y_1^2-\ldots-y_p^2+y_{p+1}^2+\ldots+y_r^2$. Then

$$T'AT = \begin{bmatrix} -I_p & 0 & 0 \\ 0 & I_{r-p} & 0 \\ 0 & 0 & 0 \end{bmatrix}.$$

Consequently (Problem 3.17) rank A = rank $T'AT = r$.

(ii) Let $\lambda_1 < 0,\ldots,\lambda_q < 0$, $\lambda_{q+1} > 0,\ldots,\lambda_s > 0$ be the non-zero eigenvalues of A. There is an orthogonal matrix T such that $x = Tw$ reduces $x'Ax$ to $\lambda_1 w_1^2+\ldots+\lambda_s w_s^2$ (§ 4.3). The further transformation

$$y_1 = w_1\sqrt{-\lambda_1},\ldots,\quad y_q = w_q\sqrt{-\lambda_q},\quad y_{q+1} = w_{q+1}\sqrt{\lambda_{q+1}},\ldots,$$
$$y_s = w_s\sqrt{\lambda_s},\quad y_{s+1} = w_{s+1},\ldots,\quad y_n = w_n$$

reduces $x'Ax$ to the normal form $-y_1^2-\ldots-y_q^2+y_{q+1}^2+\ldots+y_s^2$. Thus $x'Ax$ has index q and rank s. $\qquad\square$

Problem 5.3 Prove that a real quadratic form factorizes into real distinct linear factors if, and only if, it has rank 2 and index 0.

Solution. We prove the 'only if' part first. Thus we assume that $x'Ax = (l_1x_1+\ldots+l_nx_n)(m_1x_1+\ldots+m_nx_n) = (l'x)(m'x)$ where the column vectors l, m are not scalar multiples of each other. It follows that there are indices α, β such that the determinant $\begin{vmatrix} l_\alpha & l_\beta \\ m_\alpha & m_\beta \end{vmatrix} \neq 0$. To simplify the notation we take $\alpha = 1, \beta = 2$. The non-singular transformation $w_1 = l_1x_1+\ldots+l_nx_n$, $w_2 = m_1x_1+\ldots+m_nx_n$, $w_i = x_i$

56

$(i > 2)$ reduces the quadratic form to $w_1 w_2$. The further transformation $w_1 = y_1 + y_2$, $w_2 = -y_1 + y_2$, $w_i = y_i$ $(i > 2)$ reduces it to the normal form $-y_1^2 + y_2^2$ and proves that it has rank 2 and index 1.

To prove the 'if' part we suppose that $x'Ax$ has rank 2 and index 1. Consequently there is a non-singular transformation $y = Tx$ such that $x'Ax = -y_1^2 + y_2^2 = (y_2 + y_1)(y_2 - y_1)$. The forms $y_2 + y_1$ and $y_2 - y_1$ are linear in $x_1, \ldots, x_n$ and so $x'Ax$ is a product of linear factors. The factors are distinct because T is non-singular. $\qquad\square$

Problem 5.4 (i) Prove that a real quadratic form in n variables is positive definite if and only if it has rank n and index 0. (ii) Show that the quadratic form in 3 variables $2x_1^2 + x_2^2 + 2x_3^2 + 2x_1 x_2 + 2x_1 x_3$ is positive definite.

Solution. (i) Suppose first that the form $x'Ax$ has rank n and index 0. Then there is a non-singular transformation $x = Ty$ such that $x'Ax = y_1^2 + \ldots + y_n^2$. Consequently $x'Ax > 0$ unless $y = O$. But if $y = O$ then $x = O$ and so the form is positive definite.

Secondly we suppose that $x'Ax$ is positive definite and that it has rank r and index p. Then there is a non-singular transformation $x = Ty$ such that $x'Ax = -y_1^2 - \ldots - y_p^2 + y_{p+1}^2 + \ldots + y_r^2$. The index p is zero. For otherwise there are values of $x_1, \ldots, x_n$ such that $y_1 = 1$, $y_2 = 0, \ldots, y_n = 0$ and for these values $x'Ax = -1 < 0$. The rank $r = n$. For otherwise there are values of $x_1, \ldots, x_n$ (not all zero) such that $y_1 = 0, \ldots, y_{n-1} = 0, y_n = 1$. These values make $x'Ax = 0$ but x is not the zero vector.

(ii) We complete the square first in x_2 and then in x_1 and so express the form as $(x_2 + x_1)^2 + (x_1 + x_3)^2 + x_3^2$. The non-singular transformation $y_1 = x_2 + x_1$, $y_2 = x_1 + x_3$, $y_3 = x_3$ reduces the form to $y_1^2 + y_2^2 + y_3^2$ and it is therefore positive definite. $\qquad\square$

Problem 5.5 Prove that the real quadratic form $ax_1^2 + 2hx_1 x_2 + bx_2^2$ is definite if and only if $ab - h^2 > 0$. Show that it is then positive or negative definite according as $a > 0$ or $a < 0$.

Solution. Similar arguments to those in Problem 5.4(i) show that a real quadratic form in n variables is negative definite if and only if it has rank and index n. A real quadratic form is *definite* if it is either positive or negative definite.

The matrix of the given quadratic form in 2 variables is $A = \begin{bmatrix} a & h \\ h & b \end{bmatrix}$.

Problem 5.2(ii) shows that the form is definite if and only if the eigenvalues α, β of A are both positive or both negative, that is if and only if $\alpha\beta > 0$. But $\alpha\beta = |A| = ab - h^2$ (Problem 4.6).

If $ab - h^2 > 0$ then $ab > 0$ and so a, b are non-zero and have the same sign. Problem 4.6 shows that $\alpha + \beta = a + b$ and therefore α and β are both positive or both negative according as $a > 0$ or $a < 0$. $\quad\square$

Problem 5.6 Prove that a real symmetric matrix A is positive definite if and only if $A = P'P$ where P is a real non-singular matrix.

Solution. A real symmetric matrix A is *positive definite* if the quadratic form $x'Ax$ is positive definite. Consequently if the $n \times n$ matrix A is positive definite there is a non-singular transformation $x = Ty$ such that $x'Ax = y_1^2 + \ldots + y_n^2$. Therefore $T'AT = I$ and so $A = P'P$ where $P = T^{-1}$.

Conversely if $A = P'P$ then the non-singular transformation $y = Px$ transforms the quadratic form $x'Ax = x'P'Px$ to the normal form $y'y = y_1^2 + \ldots + y_n^2$. Therefore A is positive definite. $\quad\square$

Problem 5.7 (i) A is a symmetric positive definite matrix. Prove that there is a symmetric positive definite matrix B such that $B^2 = A$.

(ii) P is a real non-singular matrix. Prove that there is an orthogonal matrix R and a symmetric positive definite matrix S such that $P = RS$.

Solution. (i) There is an orthogonal matrix T such that $T^{-1}AT = \mathrm{diag}\{\lambda_1, \ldots, \lambda_n\}$ where $\lambda_1, \ldots, \lambda_n$ are the eigenvalues of A (§ 4.3). Because A is positive definite these eigenvalues are all positive. Define a matrix Λ by $\Lambda = \mathrm{diag}\{\sqrt{\lambda_1}, \ldots, \sqrt{\lambda_n}\}$ and put $B = T\Lambda T^{-1}$. As T is orthogonal B is symmetric. B has positive eigenvalues $\sqrt{\lambda_1}, \ldots, \sqrt{\lambda_n}$ and is therefore positive definite. Finally $B^2 = T\Lambda^2 T^{-1} = A$.

We remark that B is determined uniquely by A. It is called the square root of A.

(ii) The matrix $P'P$ is positive definite (Problem 5.6) and part (i) shows that there is a symmetric positive definite matrix S such that $S^2 = P'P$. S is non-singular and so we can put $P = PS^{-1}S = RS$ where $R = PS^{-1}$. R is orthogonal. For S^{-1} is symmetric and therefore $R'R = S^{-1}P'PS^{-1} = S^{-1}S^2S^{-1} = I$.

We remark that R and S are determined uniquely by P. $\quad\square$

5.2 The Simultaneous Reduction of Real Quadratic Forms Given two real quadratic forms $x'Ax$, $x'Bx$ in n variables $x_1, \ldots, x_n$ it is not always possible to find a real non-singular transformation $x = Ty$ which reduces both forms to diagonal forms. It is possible if one form, let us say $x'Bx$, is positive definite. For we can make a linear transformation $x = Pw$ which reduces $x'Bx$ to $w_1^2 + \ldots + w_n^2$, and then an orthogonal transformation $w = Qy$ such that $w'P'APw = \lambda_1 y_1^2 + \ldots + \lambda_n y_n^2$. It follows that

$$x'Bx = w_1^2 + \ldots + w_n^2 = y_1^2 + \ldots + y_n^2,$$
$$x'Ax = w'P'APw = \lambda_1 y_1^2 + \ldots + \lambda_n y_n^2$$

and therefore the combined transformation $x = (PQ)y$ reduces both forms simultaneously to diagonal forms.

The preceding argument does not provide a good way of finding the transformation. There is a better method which follows the procedure for the orthogonal reduction of quadratic forms given in § 4.3. To make the parallel exact we introduce another scalar product for real $n \times 1$ column vectors through the definition $\langle u, v \rangle = u'Bv$. The orthogonality and norms of vectors with respect to this scalar product are said to be wrt B.

The roots of the equation $|A - \lambda B| = 0$ are the *eigenvalues of A wrt B*. If μ is an eigenvalue then any vector v such that $(A - \mu B)v = O$ is an *eigenvector* of A wrt B.

Problem 5.8 $x'Ax$, $x'Bx$ are real quadratic forms and $x'Bx$ is positive definite.

(i) Suppose that $x = Ty$ is a real non-singular transformation which reduces $x'Bx$ to $y_1^2 + \ldots + y_n^2$ and $x'Ax$ to $\lambda_1 y_1^2 + \ldots + \lambda_n y_n^2$. Prove that $\lambda_1, \ldots, \lambda_n$ are the eigenvalues of A wrt B and that the columns of T are corresponding eigenvectors which are of norm 1 and mutually orthogonal wrt B.

(ii) Prove that eigenvectors of A wrt B belonging to distinct eigenvalues are mutually orthogonal wrt B.

Solution. (i) The matrix T satisfies the conditions $T'AT = \Lambda$, $T'BT = I$ where $\Lambda = \text{diag}\{\lambda_1, \ldots, \lambda_n\}$. It follows that $T'(A - \lambda B)T = \Lambda - \lambda I$ and so the determinants satisfy $|A - \lambda B||T|^2 = |\Lambda - \lambda I|$. This relation shows that $\lambda_1, \ldots, \lambda_n$ are the eigenvalues of A wrt B.

To prove the rest of (i) we partition T into its column vectors as $T = [v_1 \ldots v_n]$. Because T is non-singular the two conditions on T imply that $AT = BT\Lambda$. Consequently by partitioned multiplication (Problem 1.22)

$$[Av_1 \ldots Av_n] = [\lambda_1 Bv_1 \ldots \lambda_n Bv_n]$$

and so $v_1, \ldots, v_n$ are the eigenvectors of A wrt B corresponding to the eigenvalues $\lambda_1, \ldots, \lambda_n$.

Finally $I = T'BT = [v_i'Bv_j]$ and therefore $v_1, \ldots, v_n$ are of norm 1 and mutually orthogonal wrt B.

E

(ii) It is a consequence of part (i) that the eigenvalues of A wrt B are real. Let $\alpha \neq \beta$ be two such eigenvalues and u, v corresponding real eigenvectors. We multiply the relation $Au = \alpha Bu$ by v' to obtain $v'Au = \alpha v'Bu$. On the other hand $v'Au = (u'Av)' = (\beta u'Bv)' = \beta v'Bu$. Therefore, because $\alpha \neq \beta$, $v'Bu = 0$. $\qquad\square$

Problem 5.9 Find a real non-singular transformation which reduces both of the following quadratic forms to diagonal forms:
$$2x_1^2 + x_2^2 + 2x_3^2 + 2x_1 x_2 + 2x_1 x_3, \qquad x_1^2 + 2x_2^2 - x_3^2 + 4x_1 x_2 - 2x_1 x_3.$$

Solution. The matrices of the quadratic forms are respectively
$$B = \begin{bmatrix} 2 & 1 & 1 \\ 1 & 1 & 0 \\ 1 & 0 & 2 \end{bmatrix}, \qquad A = \begin{bmatrix} 1 & 2 & -1 \\ 2 & 2 & 0 \\ -1 & 0 & -1 \end{bmatrix}.$$

$x'Bx$ is positive definite (Problem 5.4(ii)) and so the simultaneous reduction is possible. According to Problem 5.8(i) we can construct T from eigenvectors of A wrt B, so chosen that they are of norm 1 and mutually orthogonal wrt B. A calculation shows that $|A - \lambda B| = -\lambda(\lambda + 1)(\lambda - 2)$ and therefore the eigenvalues of A wrt B are $-1, 2, 0$. The eigenvectors corresponding to -1 are the solutions of the equations $(A + B)u = 0$. These equations are $3u_1 + 3u_2 = 0$, $3u_1 + 3u_2 = 0$, $u_3 = 0$ and the general solution is $u_1 = -\alpha$, $u_2 = \alpha$, $u_3 = 0$ where α is arbitrary. Because $u'Bu = 2u_1^2 + u_2^2 + 2u_3^2 + 2u_1 u_2 + 2u_1 u_3 = \alpha^2$ the choice $\alpha = 1$ gives an eigenvector of norm 1 wrt B.

Similar calculations lead to eigenvectors of norm 1 wrt B corresponding to the other eigenvalues $2, 0$. As the eigenvalues are all different these three eigenvectors are mutually orthogonal wrt B (Problem 5.8(ii)). Consequently the transformation $x = Ty$ where
$$T = \begin{bmatrix} -1 & 0 & -1 \\ 1 & 1 & 1 \\ 0 & 0 & 1 \end{bmatrix}$$
will reduce the quadratic forms to $y_1^2 + y_2^2 + y_3^2$ and $-y_1^2 + 2y_2^2$ respectively. $\qquad\square$

Problem 5.10 $x'Ax$ and $x'Bx$ are real quadratic forms and $x'Bx$ is positive definite. Show that, for $x \neq 0$,
$$\lambda_1 \leqslant \frac{x'Ax}{x'Bx} \leqslant \lambda_n$$
where λ_1 and λ_n are respectively the least and greatest of the eigenvalues of A wrt B.

Solution. There is a real non-singular transformation $x = Ty$ such that, for $x \neq 0$,

$$\frac{x'Ax}{x'Bx} = \frac{\lambda_1 y_1^2 + \ldots + \lambda_n y_n^2}{y_1^2 + \ldots + y_n^2}$$

where $\lambda_1 \leqslant \lambda_2 \leqslant \ldots \leqslant \lambda_n$ are the eigenvalues of A wrt B. The right hand side of this equality is $\geqslant \lambda_1 (y_1^2 + \ldots + y_n^2)/y_1^2 + \ldots + y_n^2 = \lambda_1$ and $\leqslant \lambda_n (y_1^2 + \ldots + y_n^2)/y_1^2 + \ldots + y_n^2 = \lambda_n$. $\qquad\square$

The theory has an application to dynamics. Let $x_1, \ldots, x_n$ be co-ordinates specifying a dynamical system and let $x_1 = 0, \ldots, x_n = 0$ be a position of equilibrium. For small values of the coordinates there are approximations to the potential and kinetic energies in the form $V = k + \frac{1}{2}x'Ax$, $T = \frac{1}{2}\dot{x}'B\dot{x}$ where $\dot{x} = dx/dt$, k is a constant and A,B are constant symmetric matrices with B positive definite. Consequently there is a non-singular linear transformation $x = Sq$ such that
$$V = k + \frac{1}{2}(\lambda_1 q_1^2 + \ldots + \lambda_n q_n^2), \qquad T = \frac{1}{2}(\dot{q}_1^2 + \ldots + \dot{q}_n^2).$$

The motion of the system is determined by Lagrange's equations
$$\frac{d}{dt}\left(\frac{\partial L}{\partial \dot{q}_i}\right) - \frac{\partial L}{\partial q_i} = 0, \qquad i = 1, \ldots, n,$$

where $L = T - V$. Therefore $\ddot{q}_i + \lambda_i q_i = 0$. If the numbers $\lambda_1, \ldots, \lambda_n$ are > 0 the equilibrium is said to be *stable* and the motion is given by $q_i = C_i \sin(\sqrt{\lambda_i} t + \varepsilon_i), i = 1, \ldots, n$ where C_i, ε_i are constants determined by the initial conditions. A motion in which all except one of the normal coordinates $q_1, \ldots, q_n$ are zero is called a *normal mode* of vibration. The numbers $2\pi/\sqrt{\lambda_1}, \ldots, 2\pi/\sqrt{\lambda_n}$ are the *periods* of the normal modes. Because $\lambda_1, \ldots, \lambda_n$ are the eigenvalues of A wrt B these periods can be obtained without finding the matrix S.

Problem 5.11 A rod of mass m and length $2a$ is suspended from a point P by a string of length a attached to one end. Find the periods of the normal modes of vibration in a vertical plane.

Solution. We use the angular coordinates x_1, x_2 shown in the figure and neglect the weight of the string. A calculation shows that

$$V = -mga(\cos x_1 + \cos x_2),$$
$$T = \frac{1}{2}ma^2\{(\dot{x}_1 \cos x_1 + \dot{x}_2 \cos x_2)^2$$
$$+ (\dot{x}_1 \sin x_1 + \dot{x}_2 \sin x_2)^2 + \frac{1}{3}\dot{x}_2^2\}.$$

By using the approximation $\cos \theta = 1 - \frac{1}{2}\theta^2$ in the expression for V

61

and putting $x_1 = x_2 = 0$ in the expression for T we obtain the approximations $V = -2mga + \frac{1}{2}x'Ax$, $T = \frac{1}{2}\dot{x}'B\dot{x}$ where

$$A = mga\begin{bmatrix} 1 & 0 \\ 0 & 1 \end{bmatrix}, \qquad B = ma^2\begin{bmatrix} 1 & 1 \\ 1 & \frac{4}{3} \end{bmatrix}.$$

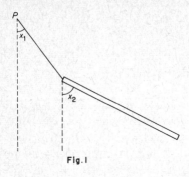

Fig. I

A calculation of $|A - \lambda B|$ shows that the periods of the normal modes are $2\pi/\sqrt{\lambda_1}$, $2\pi/\sqrt{\lambda_2}$ where λ_1, λ_2 are the roots of $a^2\lambda^2 - 7ag\lambda + 3g^2 = 0$. □

EXERCISES

1. Find a real non-singular linear transformation which reduces the quadratic form $x'Ac = x_1x_2 + x_1x_3 + x_2x_4$ to a normal form. Check your values for the rank and index by calculating the eigenvalues of A.

2. Find the error in the following argument. The quadratic form $2x_1^2 + 2x_1x_2 + 2x_1x_3$ can be expressed as $(x_1 + x_2 + x_3)^2 - (x_2 + x_3)^2 + x_1^2$ and consequently the transformation $y_1 = x_2 + x_3$, $y_2 = x_1$, $y_3 = x_1 + x_2 + x_3$ reduces it to the normal form $-y_1^2 + y_2^2 + y_3^2$. Therefore the form has rank 3 and index 1.

Obtain the correct rank and index of the quadratic form.

3. Show that the quadratic form
$$2x_1^2 + x_2^2 + 2x_3^2 + x_4^2 + 3x_1x_2 + 4x_1x_3 + 3x_1x_4 + 3x_2x_3 + 2x_2x_4 + 3x_3x_4$$
factorizes into distinct linear factors. Obtain the factors.

4. (i) Two real symmetric matrices A, B are *congruent* if $B = T'AT$ for some real non-singular matrix T. Prove that congruence is an

62

equivalence relation (see Problem 4.5(i)). Show that any two positive definite matrices of the same order are congruent.

(ii) Prove that if A is positive definite then so is A^{-1}.

5. (i) Find the square root of the positive definite matrix $\begin{bmatrix} 5 & 4 \\ 4 & 5 \end{bmatrix}$.

(ii) Express $\begin{bmatrix} 5 & -2 \\ 10 & 11 \end{bmatrix}$ as a product RS where R is orthogonal and S is positive definite.

6. $x'Ax$, $x'Bx$ are real quadratic forms where

$$A = \begin{bmatrix} 2 & -4 & -3 \\ -4 & 2 & 3 \\ -3 & 3 & 5 \end{bmatrix}, \qquad B = \begin{bmatrix} 2 & 0 & -1 \\ 0 & 2 & 1 \\ -1 & 1 & 2 \end{bmatrix}.$$

Prove that $x'Bx$ is positive definite and find a real non-singular linear transformation which reduces both forms to diagonal forms.

Find the maximum and minimum values of $x'Ax$ when it is restricted to values of x_1, x_2, x_3 such that $x'Bx = 1$.

Chapter 6

Vector Spaces

The theory of finite dimensional vector spaces provides an alternative treatment of much of the mathematics in the preceding chapters. In particular Problems 6.14, 6.16, 6.20 contain proofs of statements made in Chapter 4. The methods have the advantage that they extend to infinite dimensional spaces.

6.1 Definition We denote the real numbers by $\mathbf{R}$ and use $\in$ to mean 'is an element of'. A *real vector space* V is a set closed under operations of addition and scalar multiplication by real numbers. Thus if $u, v \in V$, $\alpha \in \mathbf{R}$ then $u + v$, αu are defined and belong to V. Further the operations are to satisfy the following axioms where $u, v, w \in V$, $\alpha, \beta \in \mathbf{R}$.

V1. $u + v = v + u$
V2. $(u + v) + w = u + (v + w)$
V3. There exists a zero $O \in V$ such that $v + O = v$ for all $v \in V$.
V4. For each $v \in V$ there exists a negative $-v \in V$ such that $v + (-v) = O$.
V5. $\alpha(\beta u) = (\alpha\beta)u$
V6. $(\alpha + \beta)u = \alpha u + \beta u$
V7. $\alpha(u + v) = \alpha u + \alpha v$
V8. $1u = u$.

An important example is the set $\mathbf{R}^n$ of all real $n \times 1$ column vectors with addition and scalar multiplication defined as in Chapter 1. More generally the set of all real matrices of a given order is a real vector space. Another familiar example is the set of all position vectors $\mathbf{OP}$ where $\mathbf{O}$ is fixed and P varies in three-dimensional euclidean space.

Problem 6.1 Show that the set V of all functions $\mathbf{R} \to \mathbf{R}$ is a real vector space.

Solution. Given $f, g \in V$, $\alpha \in \mathbf{R}$, $f + g$ is defined by $(f + g)(x) = f(x) + g(x)$ and αf by $(\alpha f)(x) = \alpha f(x)$ for all $x \in \mathbf{R}$. V is closed under these operations. The zero ϕ of V is given by $\phi(x) = 0$ for all $x \in \mathbf{R}$. The negative $-f$ of f is given by $(-f)(x) = -f(x)$ for all $x \in \mathbf{R}$. The other axioms are easily verified. For example $f + g = g + f$ because

$$(f + g)(x) = f(x) + g(x) = g(x) + f(x) = (g + f)(x). \qquad \square$$

Problem 6.2 u, v are elements in a real vector space V and $\alpha \in \mathbf{R}$.

(i) Prove that the equations $x+u = v$ and $\alpha x = u$ $(\alpha \neq 0)$ have unique solutions for x. Deduce that the zero and negative elements in V are unique.

(ii) Prove that $0u = O$, $\alpha O = O$ and deduce that $-(\alpha u) = (-\alpha)u = \alpha(-u)$.

Solution. The reader should follow each step and note the axiom used. (i) From $x+u = v$ we obtain

$$x = x+O = x+(u+(-u)) = (x+u)+(-u) = v+(-u) = v-u$$

as the unique solution where, as usual, we have written $v+(-u)$ as $v-u$. It follows that O is the only solution of the equation $x+u = u$ and that $-u$ is the only solution of $x+u = O$.

From $\alpha x = u$ we obtain

$$x = 1x = \left(\frac{1}{\alpha}\alpha\right)x = \frac{1}{\alpha}(\alpha x) = \frac{1}{\alpha}u$$

as the unique solution.

(ii) We have $0u+0u = (0+0)u = 0u$, $\alpha O+\alpha O = \alpha(O+O) = \alpha O$ and it follows from part (i) that $0u = O$, $\alpha O = O$. Consequently

$$O = 0u = (\alpha+(-\alpha))u = \alpha u+(-\alpha)u;$$
$$O = \alpha O = \alpha(u+(-u)) = \alpha u+\alpha(-u)$$

and again part (i) shows that $-(\alpha u) = (-\alpha)u = \alpha(-u)$. $\square$

Problem 6.3 Which of the following subsets are subspaces of the vector space of all functions $\mathbf{R} \to \mathbf{R}$?

The functions f such that (a) $f(0) = 0$, (b) $f(0)$ is an integer. The polynomial functions of (c) degree n, (d) degree $\leqslant n$. (e) The continuous functions. (f) The functions with derivatives of all orders.

Solution. A *subspace* of a vector space V is a subset which, with the operations of V, is itself a vector space. A subset is a subspace if and only if it is closed under addition and scalar multiplication. Consequently (a), (e), (f) are subspaces but (b), (c) are not. (d) is also a subspace provided that the zero function is included. $\square$

6.2 Linear Dependence Vectors $v_1, \ldots, v_r$ of a real vector space are *linearly dependent* if there is a relation $\alpha_1 v_1 + \ldots + \alpha_r v_r = O$ where $\alpha_1, \ldots, \alpha_r$ are real numbers which are not all zero. Otherwise the vectors are *linearly independent*. A vector v is *linearly dependent* on $v_1, \ldots, v_r$ if $v = \beta_1 v_1 + \ldots + \beta_r v_r$ for some real numbers $\beta_1, \ldots, \beta_r$. The set of all such linear combinations is a subspace called the subspace spanned by $v_1, \ldots, v_r$. For example if O, R, S are non-collinear points in euclidean space then the points P such that **OP** is linearly dependent on **OR**, **OQ** form the plane containing **O, R, Q**.

Given a set of vectors $\{v_1, \ldots, v_r\}$ we can extend any linearly independent subset to a *maximal subset* of linearly independent vectors. That is, to a linearly independent subset which is not contained in any other linearly independent subset.

A *basis* for a vector space V is an ordered set of vectors $\{v_1, \ldots, v_n\}$ which span V and are linearly independent. A vector space may not have a finite basis. But if it has a basis with n elements then any other basis also has n elements. The number n is the dimension of the vector space.

Any finite set of vectors which span a vector space V contains a basis. For a maximal subset of linearly independent vectors is automatically a basis. It follows that if V has dimension n then any n vectors which span V form a basis.

Any subset $\{w_1, \ldots, w_r\}$ of linearly independent vectors in V can be extended to form a basis. For we can choose a basis $\{v_1, \ldots, v_n\}$ for V and extend $\{w_1, \ldots, w_r\}$ to a maximal linearly independent subset of the set $\{w_1, \ldots, w_r, v_1, \ldots, v_n\}$. It follows that $r \leqslant n$ and if $r = n$ then the set $\{w_1, \ldots, w_r\}$ is already a basis.

Problem 6.4 (i) The column vectors
$$v_1 = [1, 1, 1]', \qquad v_2 = [3, 4, 5]', \qquad v_3 = [1, 2, 3]'$$
are elements of $\mathbf{R}^3$. Show that v_1, v_2 are linearly independent but that v_1, v_2, v_3 are linearly dependent. Deduce that v_3 is linearly dependent on v_1, v_2.

(ii) Show that the functions 1, t, t^2 are linearly independent.

Solution. (i) We write the equation $x_1 v_1 + x_2 v_2 = O$ as $Ax = O$ where $A = [v_1 \, v_2]$, $x = [x_1 \, x_2]'$. A has rank 2 and therefore (Problem 3.10) the only solution is $x_1 = x_2 = 0$. Consequently v_1, v_2 are linearly independent.

The equation $x_1 v_1 + x_2 v_2 + x_3 v_3 = O$ is $Bx = O$ where $B = [v_1 \, v_2 \, v_3]$, $x = [x_1 \, x_2 \, x_3]'$. Because B has rank 2 Problem 3.10 shows that there are nontrivial solutions and so v_1, v_2, v_3 are linearly dependent. Suppose $\alpha_1 v_1 + \alpha_2 v_2 + \alpha_3 v_3 = O$ is a relation of linear dependence. Then $\alpha_3 \neq 0$ because v_1, v_2 are linearly independent. Consequently $v_3 = (-\alpha_1/\alpha_3)v_1 + (-\alpha_2/\alpha_3)v_2$.

(ii) The given functions are elements of the vector space of all

66

functions $\mathbf{R} \to \mathbf{R}$. Let α, β, γ be real numbers such that $\alpha + \beta t + \gamma t^2$ is the zero function. The substitution $t = 0$ gives $\alpha = 0$. Differentiation shows that $\beta + 2\gamma t$ is the zero function and the substitution $t = 0$ gives $\beta = 0$. A second differentiation shows that $\gamma = 0$. Therefore $1, t, t^2$ are linearly independent. $\qquad\square$

Problem 6.5 (i) Show that $e_1 = [1, 0, 0]'$, $e_2 = [0, 1, 0]'$, $e_3 = [0, 0, 1]'$ form a basis for $\mathbf{R}^3$.

(ii) Show that the vector space of polynomial functions does not have a finite basis. Find the dimension of the space of polynomials of degree $\leqslant n$.

Solution. (i) The relation $x = x_1 e_1 + x_2 e_2 + x_3 e_3$ for any $x = [x_1 \; x_2 \; x_3]' \in \mathbf{R}^3$ shows that e_1, e_2, e_3 span $\mathbf{R}^3$. It also shows that e_1, e_2, e_3 are linearly independent. Consequently they form a basis.

The obvious generalization of this basis to $\mathbf{R}^n$ is called the *standard basis* of $\mathbf{R}^n$. It follows that $\mathbf{R}^n$ has dimension *n*.

(ii) If the vector space of polynomials had a finite basis with N elements then any $N + 1$ elements in the space would be linearly dependent. This is not so as the set $1, t, \ldots, t^n$ is linearly independent for all values of n. The set spans the subspace of polynomials of degree $\leqslant n$. Consequently the dimension of the subspace is $n + 1$. $\qquad\square$

Problem 6.6 Find a basis for the subspace V of $\mathbf{R}^3$ spanned by the vectors v_1, v_2, v_3 of Problem 6.4. Extend this basis to a basis for $\mathbf{R}^3$.

Solution. Problem 6.4(i) shows that $\{v_1, v_2\}$ is a maximal linearly independent subset of $\{v_1, v_2, v_3\}$. It is therefore a basis for V. Let $\{e_1, e_2, e_3\}$ be the standard basis for $\mathbf{R}^3$. We extend $\{v_1, v_2\}$ to a maximal linearly independent subset of $\{v_1, v_2, e_1, e_2, e_3\}$. A particular choice is $\{v_1, v_2, e_1\}$ and it is automatically a basis for $\mathbf{R}^3$. $\qquad\square$

Problem 6.7 Prove that the rank of a matrix is equal to the dimension of the vector space spanned by its column vectors.

Solution. Suppose that the $m \times n$ matrix A has rank r. A contains a non-singular submatrix of order $r \times r$ and the columns of this submatrix determine r column vectors of A. Problem 3.10 shows that these r column vectors are linearly independent and that for $s > r$ any s columns of A are linearly dependent. Hence the r column vectors form a maximal linearly independent subset of the column vectors of A, and therefore a basis for the vector space (a subspace of $\mathbf{R}^m$) spanned by these vectors.

Because rank A = rank A' the rank of A is also equal to the dimension of the vector space spanned by its row vectors.

We have defined rank using determinants (§ 3.2). Problem 6.7 shows that rank can also be defined in terms of linear dependence and many authors do this. $\square$

Problem 6.8 $\{u_1, \ldots, u_m\}, \{v_1, \ldots, v_n\}$ are two bases of a vector space. Use the theory of linear equations to prove that $m = n$. Prove also that

$$u_j = \sum_i a_{ij} v_i, \qquad i,j = 1, \ldots, n,$$

where $A = [o_{ij}]$ is non-singular.

Solution. We express $u_1, \ldots, u_m$ as

$$u_\alpha = \sum_i a_{i\alpha} v_i, \qquad \alpha = i, \ldots, m; i = 1, \ldots, n$$

and introduce the $n \times m$ matrix $A = [a_{i\alpha}]$. If x is a column vector such that $Ax = O$ then $x_1 u_1 + \ldots + x_m u_m = O$. Therefore, because $u_1, \ldots, u_m$ are linearly independent, Problem 3.10 shows that rank $A = m$. Consequently $n \geqslant m$. The same argument with the two bases interchanged shows that $m \geqslant n$. Therefore $m = n$. We have also proved that A is non-singular.

We remark that, conversely, if $\{v_1, \ldots, v_n\}$ is a basis and $u_j = \sum_i a_{ij} v_i$, where $A = [a_{ij}]$ is non-singular, then $\{u_1, \ldots, u_n\}$ is also a basis. $\square$

6.3 Linear Mappings

Let V, W be real vector spaces. A mapping $F: V \to W$ is a *linear mapping* if $F(u+v) = F(u) + F(v)$, $F(\alpha u) = \alpha F(u)$ for all $u, v \in V, \alpha \in \mathbf{R}$. For example if A is an $n \times m$ matrix then the mapping $L_A: \mathbf{R}^n \to \mathbf{R}^m$) defined by $L_A(x) = Ax$ is a linear mapping. The operation of differentiation defines a linear mapping $C^\infty(\mathbf{R}) \to C^\infty(\mathbf{R})$ where $C^\infty(\mathbf{R})$ is the vector space of functions $\mathbf{R} \to \mathbf{R}$ with derivatives of all orders.

The *kernel* of a linear mapping $F: V \to W$ is the set of elements $v \in V$ such that $F(v) = O$. The *range* of F is the set of elements $w \in W$ for which a v exists such that $F(v) = w$. The kernel and range are subspaces of V and W respectively.

Suppose that V has finite dimension and let $\{v_1, \ldots, v_n\}$ be a basis. The vectors $F(v_1), \ldots, F(v_n)$ will span the range of F. If we choose the basis so that $\{v_1, \ldots, v_d\}$ is a basis for the kernel of F then $F(v_1) = \ldots = F(v_d) = 0$. In this case $F(v_{d+1}), \ldots, F(v_n)$ form a basis for the range of F. Consequently

$$\dim(\text{kernel } F) + \dim(\text{range } F) = \dim V \qquad (6.1)$$

where dim stands for dimension.

Linear mappings between finite dimensional vector spaces can be expressed in terms of matrices. Let V be a vector space with basis $\{v_1, \ldots, v_n\}$. Any vector $v \in V$ can be expressed uniquely as $x_1 v_1 + \ldots + x_n v_n$. The numbers $x_1, \ldots, x_n$ are the *coordinates* of v with respect to the basis and the corresponding column vector x is the *coordinate vector* of v. Let $F: V \to W$ be a linear mapping and choose a basis $\{w_1, \ldots, w_m\}$ for W. $F(v_i)$ can be expressed uniquely as $F(v_i) = \sum_\alpha a_{\alpha i} w_\alpha$, $i = 1, \ldots, n$; $\alpha = 1, \ldots, m$. The matrix $A = [a_{\alpha i}]$ is the *matrix associated with F* (relative to the chosen bases). Because F is a linear mapping

$$F(\sum_i x_i v_i) = \sum_i x_i F(v_i) = \sum_\alpha (\sum_i x_i a_{\alpha i}) w_\alpha = \sum_\alpha y_\alpha w_\alpha \qquad (6.2)$$

where $y = Ax$. We note that in our first example the matrix associated with L_A relative to the standard bases of $\mathbf{R}^n$, $\mathbf{R}^m$ is A itself.

Problem 6.9 (i) Find the range and kernel of the differentiation operator $D: C^\infty(\mathbf{R}) \to C^\infty(\mathbf{R})$.

(ii) $L_A: \mathbf{R}^4 \to \mathbf{R}^3$ is defined by $L_A(x) = Ax$ where

$$A = \begin{bmatrix} 1 & 2 & 3 & 4 \\ 1 & 2 & 4 & 5 \\ 2 & 4 & 5 & 7 \end{bmatrix}.$$

Find the dimensions of the range and kernel of L_A and verify the relation (6.1).

Solution. (i) Given $f \in C^\infty(\mathbf{R})$ we can find by integration a function g such that $Dg = f$. Consequently the range is the whole of $C^\infty(\mathbf{R})$. The kernel is the set of constant functions.

(ii) The kernel of L_A is the set of solutions of $Ax = 0$. We find from Problem 3.3 that this set is $\{\alpha v_1 + \beta v_2\}$ where $\alpha, \beta \in \mathbf{R}$ and $v_1 = [-2, 1, 0, 0]'$, $v_2 = [1, 0, 1, -1]'$. The vectors v_1, v_2 are linearly independent and therefore $\dim(\text{kernel } L_A) = 2$.

Let $e_1, \ldots, e_4$ be the standard basis for $\mathbf{R}^4$. The range of L_A is spanned by the vectors $Ae_1, \ldots, Ae_4$ which are the column vectors of A. Because rank $A = 2$ it follows from Problem 6.7 that $\dim(\text{range } L_A) = 2$. The dimensions agree with the relation (6.1) since $\dim \mathbf{R}^4 = 4$.

We remark that if L_A is any linear mapping $\mathbf{R}^n \to \mathbf{R}^m$ then $\dim(\text{range } L_A) = \text{rank } A$. $\qquad \square$

Problem 6.10 V and W are the vector spaces of polynomials of degrees $\leqslant 3$ and $\leqslant 2$ respectively. $F:V \to W$ is differentiation. Find the matrix associated with F relative to the bases $\{1, t, t^2, t^3\}$, $\{1, t, t^2\}$.

Solution. We denote the given bases by $\{v_1, v_2, v_3, v_4\}$, $\{w_1, w_2, w_3\}$ and find that $Fv_1 = 0$, $Fv_2 = w_1$, $Fv_3 = 2w_2$, $Fv_4 = 3w_3$. The matrix A associated with F is the transpose of the matrix of coefficients of these relations and consequently

$$A = \begin{bmatrix} 0 & 1 & 0 & 0 \\ 0 & 0 & 2 & 0 \\ 0 & 0 & 0 & 3 \end{bmatrix}.$$

$\square$

Problem 6.11 $\{u_1, \ldots, u_n\}$, $\{v_1, \ldots, v_n\}$ are two bases of a vector space V so that

$$u_j = \sum_i t_{ij} v_i, \qquad i, j = 1, \ldots, n, \tag{6.3}$$

where $T = [t_{ij}]$ is non-singular. $F:V \to V$ is a linear mapping and A is its associated matrix relative to $\{v_1, \ldots, v_n\}$. Prove that its associated matrix relative to $\{u_1, \ldots, u_n\}$ is $T^{-1}AT$.

Verify this relation when V is the vector space of functions $a + b\,e^t + c\,e^{-t}$ $(a, b, c \in \mathbf{R})$, F is differentiation and the two bases are $\{1, e^t, \cosh t\}$, $\{1, e^{-t}, \sinh t\}$.

Solution. F is a linear mapping of V into itself and so there is an associated matrix relative to a single basis. Thus $A = [a_{ij}]$ where $F(v_i) = \sum_j a_{ji} v_j$, $i, j = 1, \ldots, n$. We find from the relation (6.3) that $v_k = \sum_h s_{hk} u_h$, $h, k = 1, \ldots, n$, where $S = [s_{hk}]$ is the inverse of T. Consequently, because F is a linear mapping,

$$F(u_j) = \sum_i t_{ij} F(v_i) = \sum_{i,k} t_{ij} a_{ki} v_k$$

$$= \sum_{i,k,h} t_{ij} a_{ki} s_{hk} u_h = \sum_h \left(\sum_{i,k} s_{hk} a_{ki} t_{ij} \right) u_h.$$

Therefore the matrix associated with F relative to $\{u_1, \ldots, u_n\}$ is $T^{-1}AT$.

To deal with the particular case we denote the given bases by $\{u_1, u_2, u_3\}$, $\{v_1, v_2, v_3\}$. We find that $u_1 = v_1$, $u_2 = v_2 + 2v_3$, $u_3 = v_2 + v_3$. Consequently, because T is the transpose of the matrix of coefficients of $v_1, \ldots, v_n$ in (6.3),

$$T = \begin{bmatrix} 1 & 0 & 0 \\ 0 & 1 & 1 \\ 0 & 2 & 1 \end{bmatrix}.$$

The relations $Fu_1 = 0$, $Fu_2 = u_2$, $Fu_3 = u_2 - u_3$; $Fv_1 = 0$, $Fv_2 = -v_2$,

$Fv_3 = v_2 + v_3$ show that the matrices associated with F are respectively

$$B = \begin{bmatrix} 0 & 0 & 0 \\ 0 & 1 & 1 \\ 0 & 0 & -1 \end{bmatrix}, \quad A = \begin{bmatrix} 1 & 0 & 0 \\ 0 & -1 & 1 \\ 0 & 0 & 1 \end{bmatrix}.$$

It is easy to verify that $B = T^{-1}AT$. $\qquad\square$

There is an algebra of linear mappings corresponding to the algebra of matrices. Given linear mappings $G:U \to V$, $F, H:V \to W$ and $\alpha \in R$ we define mappings $\alpha F:V \to W$, $F+H:V \to W$, $FG:U \to W$ by

$$(aF)(v) = aF(v), \qquad (F+H)(v) = F(v)+H(v), \qquad (FG)(u) = F(G(u))$$

for all $u \in U, v \in V$. These mappings are linear mappings. The mapping FG is the *composition* of F and G.

Suppose that bases have been chosen for U, V and W and denote the matrices associated with F, G, H by A, B, C respectively. Then the matrices associated with αF, $F+H$, FG are αA, $A+C$, AB.

The algebra of linear mappings obeys laws corresponding to the laws of matrix algebra. For example, the composition of mappings is associative.

Problem 6.12 $G:U \to V$, $F:V \to W$ are linear mappings between finite dimensional vector spaces. Prove that rank $FG \leqslant$ the smallest of rank F, rank G.

Solution. The *rank* of a linear mapping is the dimension of its range. Because $FG(u) = F(G(u))$ the range of FG is a subspace of the range of F. Therefore rank $FG \leqslant$ rank F. If $G(u) = O$ then $FG(u) = O$ and so the kernel of G is a subspace of the kernel of FG. We put dim $U = l$ and use the relation (6.1) to obtain $l -$ rank $G \leqslant l -$ rank FG. Therefore rank $FG \leqslant$ rank G.

Problem 3.18(i) can be deduced from Problem 6.12 by applying the inequality to the mappings L_A, L_B. (Note that rank $L_A =$ rank A). $\quad\square$

6.4 Linear Operators A linear mapping F of a real vector space V into itself is called a linear operator. A real number μ is an eigenvalue of F if there is a non-zero vector v such that $Fv = \mu v$. Any vector u such that $Fu = \mu u$ is an eigenvector belonging to μ. Suppose that V is finite dimensional and choose a basis for V. Let A be the matrix associated with F relative to this basis. The relation (6.2) shows that μ is an eigenvalue of

71

F if and only if it is a real eigenvalue of A. Further, u is an eigenvector of F belonging to μ if and only if its coordinate vector is an eigenvector of A belonging to μ.

We define the *determinant* of F by $\det F = \det A$. Because $\det(T^{-1}AT) = \det A$, Problem 6.11 shows that the definition is independent of the choice of basis. Let I denote the identity operator $V \to V$. The *characteristic polynomial* ϕ of F is defined by $\phi(\lambda) = \det(F - \lambda I)$. It is the characteristic polynomial of any associated matrix.

Given a real polynomial $f(\lambda) = a_0\lambda^m + \ldots + a_{m-1}\lambda + a_m$ we use the operations defined at the end of § 6.3 to form $f(F) = a_0 F^m + \ldots + a_{m-1}F + a_m I$. Statements in § 6.3 imply that $f(A)$ is the matrix associated with $f(F)$ relative to the chosen basis. This remark and the Cayley–Hamilton Theorem show that $\phi(F) = O$ (the zero operator). The idea of a *minimum polynomial* (§ 4.4) is applicable to linear operators. The minimum polynomials of F and any associated matrix are the same.

A basis $\{w_1, \ldots, w_n\}$ of V diagonalizes F if $Fw_i = \mu_i w_i$, $i = 1, \ldots, n$. The vectors $w_1, \ldots, w_n$ are n linearly independent eigenvectors of F. Conversely, if F has $n = \dim V$ linearly independent eigenvectors then these necessarily form a basis of V which diagonalizes F. The associated matrix of F relative to $\{w_1, \ldots, w_n\}$ is diagonal. It follows from Problem 6.11 that F can be diagonalized if and only if any associated matrix is similar to a real diagonal matrix.

Theorems on linear operators applied to $L_A : \mathbf{R}^n \to \mathbf{R}^n$ yield theorems on matrices. For example, because A is associated with L_A relative to the standard basis of $\mathbf{R}^n$ and the eigenvectors of L_A are those of A, it follows that the $n \times n$ matrix A is similar to a diagonal matrix if and only if it has n linearly independent eigenvectors.

Problem 6.13   (i) Find the eigenvalues and eigenvectors of the differentiation operator $D : C^\infty(\mathbf{R}) \to C^\infty(\mathbf{R})$.

(ii) V is the vector space of polynomials of degree $\leqslant 2$ and $F : V \to V$ is $t^2D + D$ where D denotes differentiation. Find the matrix associated with F relative to the basis $\{1, t, t^2\}$ and use it to find the eigenvalues and eigenvectors of F. Can F be diagonalized?

Solution. (i) μ is an eigenvalue if there is a function f (not the zero function) such that $Df = \mu f$. Consequently any $\mu \in \mathbf{R}$ is an eigenvalue and the corresponding eigenvectors are the functions $ae^{\mu t}$ ($a \in \mathbf{R}$).

(ii) We denote the given basis by $\{v_1, v_2, v_3\}$ and find that $Fv_1 = O$, $Fv_2 = v_1$, $Fv_3 = 2v_2 + 2v_3$. The matrix associated with F is therefore

$$A = \begin{bmatrix} 0 & 1 & 0 \\ 0 & 0 & 2 \\ 0 & 0 & 2 \end{bmatrix}.$$

The eigenvalues of A (and of F) are 0, 0, 2. The eigenvectors of A corresponding to the eigenvalues 0 and 2 are $\alpha[1,0,0]'$ and $\beta[1,2,2]'$ where α,β are arbitrary. The eigenvectors of F are therefore $\alpha v_1 = \alpha$ and $\beta(v_1 + 2v_2 + 2v_3) = \beta(1 + 2t + 2t^2)$.

F cannot be diagonalized because it does not have three linearly independent eigenvectors. $\qquad\qquad\square$

Problem 6.14 $F:V \to V$ is a linear operator. Prove that non-zero eigenvectors of F which belong to distinct eigenvalues are linearly independent. Deduce that if F has dim V distinct eigenvalues then it can be diagonalized.

Solution. Let $v_1,\ldots,v_r$ be the eigenvectors of F belonging to the distinct eigenvalues $\lambda_1,\ldots,\lambda_r$, and suppose that they are numbered so that $v_1,\ldots,v_m$ form a maximal subset of linearly independent vectors. If $m < r$ then $v_{m+1} = \alpha_1 v_1 + \ldots + \alpha_m v_m$ where $\alpha_1,\ldots,\alpha_m$ are not all zero. The relation $Fv_{m+1} = \lambda_{m+1} v_{m+1}$ implies that

$$\alpha_1 \lambda_1 v_1 + \ldots + \alpha_m \lambda_m v_m = \lambda_{m+1} (\alpha_1 v_1 + \ldots + \alpha_m v_m).$$

Consequently, because $v_1,\ldots,v_m$ are linearly independent and $\lambda_{m+1} \neq \lambda_1,\ldots,\lambda_m$ the numbers $\alpha_1,\ldots,\alpha_m$ are all zero. This contradiction proves that $m = r$.

If F has $n = $ dim V distinct eigenvalues then any n corresponding non-zero eigenvectors are linearly independent. They form a basis which diagonalizes F. The corresponding result for matrices is that a real $n \times n$ matrix A with n distinct real eigenvalues is similar to a diagonal matrix. $\qquad\qquad\square$

Problem 6.15 (i) $F:V \to V$ is a linear operator on an n-dimensional vector space. Prove that the geometric multiplicity of an eigenvalue of F is $\leqslant$ the algebraic multiplicity.

(ii) Calculate the algebraic and geometric multiplicities of L_A, L_B: $\mathbf{R}^3 \to \mathbf{R}^3$ where A and B are the matrices in Problem 4.4.

Solution. (i) The *algebraic multiplicity* of an eigenvalue μ of F is the power to which the factor $\lambda - \mu$ occurs in the characteristic polynomial $\phi(\lambda)$ of F. The *geometric multiplicity* is the dimension of the subspace formed by the eigenvectors belonging to μ. This subspace is called the *eigenspace* of μ.

Let r be the geometric multiplicity of μ and choose a basis $v_1, \ldots, v_n$ for V such that $v_1, \ldots, v_r$ form a basis for the eigenspace of μ. The matrix associated with F relative to this basis can be partitioned as $\begin{bmatrix} \mu I_r & B \\ O & C \end{bmatrix}$.

The characteristic polynomial of this matrix and hence of F is $(\mu - \lambda)^r |C - \lambda I_{n-r}|$. Consequently the factor $\lambda - \mu$ occurs at least to the power r.

(ii) The calculations have been done in Problem 4.4. L_A has eigenvalues 0, 1 with algebraic (geometric) multiplicities 1(1), 2(1) respectively. L_B has eigenvalues 0, 1 with algebraic (geometric) multiplicities 1(1), 2(2) respectively. $\qquad \square$

Problem 6.16 $F:V \to V$ is a linear operator on an n-dimensional vector space. Prove that if a minimum polynomial of F factorizes into distinct linear factors then F can be diagonalized.

Solution. Let $\psi = (\lambda - \lambda_1) \cdots (\lambda - \lambda_k)$ be a minimum polynomial of F. The numbers $\lambda_1, \ldots, \lambda_k$ are eigenvalues of F and we choose a basis for each corresponding eigenspace. It follows from Problem 6.14 that the union of these bases is a set of linearly independent eigenvectors. The set is a basis for V. For we will show that any $v \in V$ can be expressed as $v = v_1 + \ldots + v_k$ where each v_r is an eigenvector belonging to λ_r.

To do this we use the polynomials ψ_r obtained from ψ by omitting the factor $\lambda - \lambda_r$. Because $\psi_r(\lambda_r) \neq 0$ we can define the polynomial $1 - \sum_r a_r \psi_r(\lambda)$, $r = 1, \ldots, k$ where $a_r = 1/\psi_r(\lambda_r)$. This polynomial is of degree $\leqslant k - 1$ and yet has k roots $\lambda_1, \ldots, \lambda_k$. Consequently it is the zero polynomial. Thus, when we form the corresponding polynomial in F we get a zero operator and therefore $I = \sum_r a_r \psi_r(F)$. It follows that for any $v \in V$,

$$v = Iv = \sum_r a_r \psi_r(F)v = \sum_r v_r.$$

The vector v_r is an eigenvector belonging to λ_r because $(F - \lambda_r I)v_r = (F - \lambda_r I)(a_r \psi_r(F)v) = a_r \psi(F)v = O$.

We have proved that V has a basis of eigenvectors and so F can be diagonalized. $\qquad \square$

6.5 Euclidean Vector Spaces A *euclidean vector space* is a real vector space V with a *scalar product*. That is, for each ordered pair $u, v \in V$ there is a real number $\langle u, v \rangle$ such that

$$E1\langle u+v, w\rangle = \langle u, w\rangle + \langle v, w\rangle \qquad E2\langle \alpha u, v\rangle = \alpha(u, v) \quad \text{for } \alpha \in \mathbf{R}$$
$$E3\langle u, v\rangle = \langle v, u\rangle \qquad\qquad\qquad E4\langle u, u\rangle \leqslant 0 \quad \text{and is } > 0$$
$$\text{if } u \neq O.$$

The idea arises from euclidean geometry. The example to bear in mind is $\mathbf{R}^n$ with $\langle x, y\rangle = x'y$. This is the *standard euclidean structure* on $\mathbf{R}^n$. An infinite dimensional example is the vector space of real valued continuous functions on the interval $[0, 1]$ with $\langle f, g\rangle = \int_0^1 fg\, dt$.

The *norm* of $u \in V$ is $\langle u, u\rangle^{\frac{1}{2}}$. Vectors u, v are *orthogonal* if $\langle u, v\rangle = 0$. If $v_1, \ldots, v_r$ are non-zero and mutually orthogonal then they are linearly independent. For a relation $\alpha_1 v_1 + \ldots + \alpha_r v_r = O$ implies that
$$0 = \langle v_i, \alpha_1 v_1 + \ldots + \alpha_r v_r\rangle = \alpha_i \langle v_i, {}_i\rangle, \qquad i = 1, \ldots, r$$
and therefore $\alpha_i = 0$.

An *orthogonal basis* is one whose elements are mutually orthogonal. Such a basis is *orthonormal* if its elements have norm 1. Any basis of V can be modified to give an orthonormal basis (see Problem 6.17).

A linear operator $F: V \to V$ is *symmetric* if $\langle Fu, v\rangle = \langle u, Fv\rangle$ for all $u, v \in V$.

Problem 6.17 Regard $\mathbf{R}^4$ as a euclidean vector space in the standard way. Use the Gram–Schmidt process to construct an orthogonal basis for the subspace W of $\mathbf{R}^4$ spanned by
$$v_1 = [1, 0, 1, 1]', \qquad v_2 = [1, 1, 0, 1]', \qquad v_3 = [1, 1, 1, 0]'.$$
Solution. $\{v_1, v_2, v_3\}$ is a basis for W and we construct an orthogonal basis $\{u_1, u_2, u_3\}$ by $u_1 = v_1$, $u_2 = v_2 + \alpha u_1$, $u_3 = v_3 + \beta u_1 + \gamma u_2$, where we choose α, β, γ so that u_1, u_2, u_3 are mutually orthogonal. Consequently
$$\alpha = -\langle v_2, u_1\rangle / \langle u_1, u_1\rangle = -\tfrac{2}{3}, \qquad \beta = -\langle v_3, u_1\rangle / \langle u_1, u_1\rangle = -\tfrac{2}{3},$$
$$\gamma = -\langle v_3, u_2\rangle / \langle u_2, u_2\rangle = -\tfrac{2}{5},$$
and therefore $u_1 = [1, 0, 1, 1]'$, $u_2 = \tfrac{1}{3}[1, 3, -2, 1]'$, $u_3 = \tfrac{1}{5}[1, 3, 3, -4]'$.

To get an orthonormal basis we have only to divide each u_i by its norm. $\qquad\square$

Problem 6.18 $\{v_1, \ldots, v_n\}$ is an orthonormal basis of a euclidean vector space V. $\{u_1, \ldots, u_n\}$ is another basis and consequently
$$u_j = \sum_i t_{ij} v_i, \qquad i, j = 1, \ldots, n$$
where $T = [t_{ij}]$ is non-singular. Prove that $\{u_1, \ldots, u_n\}$ is orthonormal if and only if T is orthogonal.

F

$F:V \rightarrow V$ is a linear operator and A is its matrix relative to the basis $\{v_1, \ldots, v_n\}$. Prove that F is symmetric if and only if A is symmetric.

Solution. $\{u_1, \ldots, u_n\}$ is orthonormal if $\langle u_j, u_k \rangle = \delta_{jk}$, $j, k = 1, \ldots, n$. Because $\{v_1, \ldots, v_n\}$ is orthonormal this condition is

$$\delta_{jk} = \langle \sum_i t_{ij} v_i, \sum_h t_{hk} v_h \rangle = \sum_i t_{ij} t_{ik}$$

or $T'T = I$.

F is symmetric if and only if $\langle Fv_i, v_j \rangle = \langle v_i, Fv_j \rangle$, $i, j = 1, \ldots, n$. This condition is $\langle \sum_k a_{ki} v_k, v_j \rangle = \langle v_i, \sum_k a_{kj} v_k \rangle$ or because $\{v_1, \ldots, v_n\}$

is orthonormal, $a_{ji} = a_{ij}$. $\qquad\square$

Problem 6.19 $F:V \rightarrow V$ is a symmetric linear operator on an n-dimensional euclidean vector space.

(i) Prove that eigenvectors of F belonging to distinct eigenvalues are orthogonal.

(ii) Prove that the geometric and algebraic multiplicities of an eigenvalue μ of F are equal.

Solution. (i) Suppose that $Fu = \mu u$, $Fv = vv$. Then

$$\mu\langle u, v \rangle = \langle Fu, v \rangle = \langle u, Fv \rangle = v\langle u, v \rangle$$

and, because $\mu \neq v$, $\langle u, v \rangle = 0$.

(ii) Let r be the geometric multiplicity of μ and choose an orthonormal basis $\{v_1, \ldots, v_n\}$ for V such that $\{v_1, \ldots, v_r\}$ is a basis for the eigenspace of μ. For $s = 1, \ldots, r$; $\alpha = r+1, \ldots, n$ we have $\langle Fv_\alpha, v_s \rangle = \langle v_\alpha, Fv_s \rangle = \mu\langle v_\alpha, v_s \rangle = 0$. Therefore

$$Fv_\alpha = \sum_\beta c_{\beta\alpha} v_\beta, \qquad \beta = r+1, \ldots, n. \tag{6.4}$$

Consequently the matrix associated with F relative to $\{v_1, \ldots, v_n\}$ is of the form $\begin{bmatrix} \mu I_r & O \\ O & C \end{bmatrix}$ and the characteristic polynomial $\phi(\lambda)$ of F is $(\mu - \lambda)^r |C - \lambda I_{n-r}|$. In contrast to Problem 6.15(i) we can prove that $\mu - \lambda$ is not a factor of $|C - \lambda I_{n-r}|$ and this will complete the solution.

Let W be the subspace spanned by $v_{r+1}, \ldots, v_n$. The relation (6.4) shows that F transforms W into itself and therefore determines a linear operator $\tilde{F}:W \rightarrow W$. The matrix associated with $\tilde{F}$ relative to $\{v_{r+1}, \ldots, v_n\}$ is C and the characteristic polynomial of $\tilde{F}$ is $|C - \lambda I_{n-r}|$. If this polynomial had a factor $\mu - \lambda$, W would contain a non-zero eigenvector w of $\tilde{F}$ (and hence of F) belonging to the eigenvalue μ. But no such w can exist as the only vector in both W and the eigenspace of μ is zero. $\qquad\square$

Problem 6.20 $F: V \to V$ is a symmetric linear operator on an n-dimensional euclidean vector space. Prove that F can be diagonalized by an orthonormal basis.

Deduce that if A is a real symmetric $n \times n$ matrix then there is an orthogonal matrix T such that $T^{-1}AT$ is diagonal.

Solution. Problems 6.18 and 4.11(i) show that the characteristic polynomial of F factorizes into linear factors. Choose an orthonormal basis in each eigenspace. Problem 6.19(ii) implies that the union of these bases contains n vectors. Problem 6.19(i) implies that the n vectors are mutually orthogonal. They are necessarily linearly independent and therefore form an orthonormal basis of V composed of eigenvectors of F.

A is the associated matrix of L_A relative to the standard orthonormal basis $\{e_1, \ldots, e_n\}$ of $\mathbf{R}^n$. Therefore L_A is symmetric and $\mathbf{R}^n$ admits an orthonormal basis $\{v_1, \ldots, v_n\}$ composed of eigenvectors of L_A. The relations $v_j = \sum_i t_{ij} e_i$, $i, j = 1, \ldots, n$ yield an orthogonal matrix $T = [t_{ij}]$ such that $T^{-1}AT$ is diagonal.

Note that $T = [v_1 \ldots v_n]$. The existence of T was stated previously in § 4.3. $\square$

6.6 Unitary Vector Spaces The definition of a *complex vector space* is as in § 6.1 with $\mathbf{R}$ replaced by the set of complex numbers $\mathbf{C}$. The set $\mathbf{C}^n$ of complex column vectors of order $n \times 1$ is an example of an n-dimensional complex vector space. The standard basis $\{e_1, \ldots, e_n\}$ of $\mathbf{R}^n$ is also the standard basis of $\mathbf{C}^n$.

The ideas of linear dependence and linear mapping extend in an obvious way to the complex case. Indeed the theory of linear operators becomes simpler because any complex polynomial factorizes into complex linear factors. Of course these factors may not be distinct.

There is an important extension of the idea of a euclidean vector space which is not so obvious. A *unitary vector space* V is a complex vector space with a scalar product. That is, for each ordered pair $u, v \in V$ there is a complex number $\langle u, v \rangle$ such that

U1. $\langle u+v, w \rangle = \langle u, w \rangle + \langle v, w \rangle$ U2. $\langle \alpha u, v \rangle = \alpha \langle u, v \rangle$

$$\text{for } \alpha \in \mathbf{C}$$

U3. $\langle u, v \rangle = \overline{\langle v, u \rangle}$ U4. $\langle u, u \rangle \geqslant 0$ and is

$$> 0 \text{ if } u \neq O.$$

An example of such a space is $\mathbf{C}^n$ with its standard unitary structure

$\langle x, y \rangle = x'\bar{y}$. Note that the scalar product is not symmetric. The reader should deduce from the axioms that

$$\langle w, u+v \rangle = \langle w, u \rangle + \langle w, v \rangle, \qquad \langle u, \alpha v \rangle = \bar{\alpha} \langle u, v \rangle.$$

The definitions of orthogonality and norm apply at once to unitary space. The method of Problem 6.18 can be used to show that two orthonormal bases $\{u_1, \ldots, u_n\}$, $\{v_1, \ldots, v_n\}$ are related by $u_j = \sum_i t_{ij} v_i$ where $T = [t_{ij}]$ is a unitary matrix.

The *adjoint* F^* of a linear operator $F : V \to V$ is determined by the condition $\langle Fu, v \rangle = \langle u, F^* v \rangle$ for all $u, v \in V$. Again the method of Problem 6.18 can be used to show that if A is the matrix associated with F relative to an orthonormal basis then $\bar{A}'$ is the matrix associated with F^*. F is *normal* if $FF^* = F^*F$. Normal operators include *hermitian* ($F^* = F$), *skew-hermitian* ($F^* = -F$) and *unitary* ($F^* = F^{-1}$). F is normal if and only if A is a normal matrix i.e. $A\bar{A}' = \bar{A}'A$.

Problem 6.21 $F : V \to V$ is a normal operator on a unitary vector space. Show that $J = F - \mu I$ is also a normal operator. Deduce that if $Fw = \mu w$ then $F^* w = \bar{\mu} w$.

Solution. I is the identity operator and $\mu \in \mathbf{C}$. Consequently

$$\langle Ju, v \rangle = \langle Fu, v \rangle - \mu \langle u, v \rangle = \langle u, F^* v \rangle - \langle u, \bar{\mu} v \rangle = \langle u, (F^* - \bar{\mu} I)v \rangle$$

for all $u, v \in V$. It follows that $J^* = F^* - \bar{\mu} I$. Because $FF^* = F^*F$ it is easy to check that $JJ^* = J^*J$.

We use the facts that J is normal and $Jw = O$ to obtain

$$\langle J^* w, J^* w \rangle = \langle JJ^* w, w \rangle = \langle J^* Jw, w \rangle = \langle O, w \rangle = 0.$$

Therefore $J^* w = O$ and hence $F^* w = \bar{\mu} w$. $\qquad\qquad\square$

Problem 6.22 $F : V \to V$ is a normal operator on a unitary vector space.

(i) Prove that eigenvectors of F belonging to distinct eigenvalues are orthogonal.

(ii) Prove that if u is an eigenvector of F and $\langle w, u \rangle = 0$ then $\langle Fw, u \rangle = 0$.

Solution. The solutions to both parts depend on Problem 6.21.

(i) Suppose that $Fu = \mu u$, $Fv = vv$. Then

$$\mu \langle u, v \rangle = \langle Fu, v \rangle = \langle u, F^* v \rangle = \langle u, vv \rangle = v \langle u, v \rangle$$

and, because $\mu \neq v$, $\langle u, v \rangle = 0$.

(ii) $\langle Fw, u \rangle = \langle w, F^* u \rangle = \langle w, \bar{\mu} u \rangle = \mu \langle w, u \rangle = 0$.

Problem 6.22(ii) can be used to extend Problem 6.19(ii) to normal operators. Problem 6.22(i) is already the extension of Problem 6.19(i).

Consequently it is possible to use the argument in Problem 6.20 to prove that a normal operator on a finite dimensional vector space can be diagonalized by an orthonormal basis. The corresponding result for matrices is that if A is a normal matrix then there is a unitary matrix U such that $U^{-1} AU$ is diagonal. □

Problem 6.23 $L_A : \mathbf{C}^3 \to \mathbf{C}^3$ is defined by $L_A(z) = Az$ where

$$A = \begin{bmatrix} 5 & -2i & 4 \\ 2i & 8 & -2i \\ 4 & 2i & 5 \end{bmatrix}.$$

Show that L_A is hermitian with respect to the standard unitary structure on $\mathbf{C}^3$, and find an orthonormal basis which diagonalizes L_A. Construct a unitary matrix U such that $U^{-1}AU$ is diagonal.

Solution. A is associated with L_A relative to the standard basis $\{e_1, e_2, e_3\}$. Because this basis is orthonormal L_A is hermitian if and only if A is hermitian. We check that $\bar{A}' = A$. Consequently L_A is normal and can be diagonalized by an orthonormal basis of eigenvectors.

The characteristic polynomial of L_A is $-\lambda^3 + 18\lambda^2 - 81\lambda$ and the eigenvalues are therefore 0, 9, 9. We have to find an eigenvector v_1 of norm 1 belonging to the eigenvalue 0 and an orthonormal basis $\{v_2, v_3\}$ for the eigenspace of 9. To obtain $\{v_2, v_3\}$ we first choose a basis for the eigenspace of 9 and then modify it by the Gram–Schmidt process. Our results are

$$v_1 = \frac{1}{3}[-2, i, 2]', \qquad v_2 = \frac{1}{\sqrt{2}}[1, 0, 1]', \qquad v_3 = \frac{1}{3\sqrt{2}}[-i, 4, i]'.$$

The matrix $U = [v_1 \, v_2 \, v_3]$ is unitary and $U^{-1}AU = \mathrm{diag}\{0, 9, 9\}$. □

6.7 The Jordan Normal Form

Let F denote a linear operator on a real or complex n-dimensional vector space V and, in the real case, suppose that the characteristic polynomial of F factorizes into real linear factors. If the geometric multiplicity of an eigenvalue of F is less than its algebraic multiplicity then there is no basis which diagonalizes F. But there is a generalization which we call a Jordan basis and which still gives a simple associated matrix.

Let μ denote an eigenvalue of F whose geometric multiplicity q is less than its algebraic multiplicity r. Let v be a non-zero eigenvector belonging to μ. A chain of vectors starting from v is a sequence $v, v_1, v_2, \ldots$ such that

$$(F - \mu I)v = 0, \qquad (F - \mu I)v_1 = v, \qquad (F - \mu I)v_2 = v_1, \ldots$$

where I is the identity operator. The chain may consist of v only. But it is possible to find q linearly independent eigenvectors such that the corresponding chains provide r linearly independent vectors. A *Jordan basis* consists of the n vectors obtained in this way using all the eigenvalues. The matrix of F relative to the Jordan basis is a *Jordan normal form*.

Problem 6.24 $L_A : \mathbf{R}^4 \to \mathbf{R}^4$ is defined by $L_A(x) = Ax$ where

$$A = \begin{bmatrix} 0 & -2 & 2 & -1 \\ 2 & 3 & -1 & 1 \\ 2 & 1 & 1 & 1 \\ 4 & 3 & -3 & 4 \end{bmatrix}.$$

Find a Jordan basis for L_A and construct a matrix T such that $T^{-1}AT$ is a Jordan normal form.

Solution. The characteristic polynomial of L_A is $|A - \lambda I| = (\lambda - 2)^4$ where I is now the 4×4 unit matrix. Therefore L_A has just one eigenvalue 2. To find the corresponding eigenspace we must solve the equation $(A - 2I)x = 0$. But to construct a chain we need to solve equations of the form $(A - 2I)x = h$ and so we consider this more general case. We find by the methods of Chapter 3 that the equations admit solutions if and only if

$$h_2 - h_3 = 0, \qquad h_1 - h_2 + h_4 = 0 \qquad (6.5)$$

and that the general solution is then

$$x_1 = -\tfrac{1}{2}\alpha + \tfrac{1}{2}h_1 + h_2, \qquad x_2 = \beta - h_1 - h_2, \qquad x_3 = \beta, \quad x_4 = \alpha \qquad (6.6)$$

where α, β are arbitrary.

The eigenspace consists of the vectors $u = [-\tfrac{1}{2}\alpha, \beta, \beta, \alpha]'$ and is of dimension 2. The equations (6.5) show that a chain starting with u can be continued if and only if $\alpha = 2\beta$. We construct a chain starting with the eigenvector $v = [-1, 1, 1, 2]'$. The equations (6.6) show that the general solution to $(A - 2I)x = v$ is $x_1 = -\tfrac{1}{2}\alpha' + \tfrac{1}{2}$, $x_2 = \beta'$, $x_3 = \beta'$. $x_4 = \alpha'$ where α', β' are arbitrary. According to the equations (6.5) a chain containing this solution can be continued if and only if $1 + \alpha' = 2\beta'$. We choose $v_1 = [0, 1, 1, 1]'$. The chain cannot be continued beyond v_2 and we choose $v_2 = [1, 0, 1, 0]'$.

The Jordan basis is completed by the choice of a second eigenvector w linearly independent of v. Our chosen basis consists of $v, v_1, v_2, w =$

$[0, 1, 1, 0]'$. It is such that

$$Av = 2v, \qquad Av_1 = 2v_1 + v, \qquad Av_2 = 2v_2 + v_1, \qquad Aw = 2w.$$

The matrix associated with L_A relative to this basis is the Jordan normal form

$$J = \begin{bmatrix} 2 & 1 & 0 & 0 \\ 0 & 2 & 1 & 0 \\ 0 & 0 & 2 & 0 \\ 0 & 0 & 0 & 2 \end{bmatrix}$$

and the matrix $T = [v\, v_1\, v_2\, w]$ satisfies $T^{-1}AT = J$. $\qquad\square$

Problem 6.25 Solve the simultaneous differential equations $dx/dt = Ax$ where A is the matrix in Problem 6.24.

Solution. We substitute $x = Ty$ where T is the matrix constructed in Problem 6.24. It follows that $dy/dt = T^{-1}ATy$ or

$$\frac{dy_1}{dt} = 2y_1 + y_2, \qquad \frac{dy_2}{dt} = 2y_2 + y_3, \qquad \frac{dy_3}{dt} = 2y_3, \qquad \frac{dy_4}{dt} = 2y_4.$$

We solve for y_4, y_3, y_2, y_1 in that order and obtain

$$y_1 = (a + bt + \tfrac{1}{2}ct^2)e^{2t}, \qquad y_2 = (b + ct)e^{2t},$$
$$y_3 = c\,e^{2t}, \qquad y_4 = d\,e^{2t}$$

where a, b, c, d are arbitrary constants. The general solution for x can be found from the relation $x = Ty$. $\qquad\square$

Problem 6.26 Classify the 2×2 and 3×3 complex matrices which satisfy $X^2 = O$.

Solution. Given any 2×2 or 3×3 complex matrix X we can find a complex matrix C such that $C^{-1}XC = J$ where J is one of the Jordan normal forms

$$\begin{bmatrix} \alpha & 0 \\ 0 & \beta \end{bmatrix}, \quad \begin{bmatrix} \alpha & 1 \\ 0 & \alpha \end{bmatrix}, \quad \begin{bmatrix} \alpha & 0 & 0 \\ 0 & \beta & 0 \\ 0 & 0 & \gamma \end{bmatrix}, \quad \begin{bmatrix} \alpha & 1 & 0 \\ 0 & \alpha & 0 \\ 0 & 0 & \beta \end{bmatrix}, \quad \begin{bmatrix} \alpha & 1 & 0 \\ 0 & \alpha & 1 \\ 0 & 0 & \alpha \end{bmatrix}$$

The only normal forms whose squares are zero are the zero matrices and

$$J_1 = \begin{bmatrix} 0 & 1 \\ 0 & 0 \end{bmatrix}, \qquad J_2 = \begin{bmatrix} 0 & 1 & 0 \\ 0 & 0 & 0 \\ 0 & 0 & 0 \end{bmatrix}.$$

Because $X^2 = O$ if and only if $J^2 = O$, the solutions to $X^2 = O$ are the zero matrices and those matrices which are similar to J_1 or J_2. $\square$

EXERCISES

1. Find a basis for the subspace W of $\mathbf{R}^4$ spanned by $[1, 2, -1, 3]'$, $[0, -2, 1, -1]'$, $[2, 2, -1, 5]'$ and extend it to a basis of $\mathbf{R}^4$. Show that $[3, 4, -2, 8]'$ lies in W.

2. The matrix A in Problem 3.8 has rank 3. Find a basis for
   (i) the subspace of $\mathbf{R}^4$ spanned by the column vectors of A,
   (ii) the subspace of $\mathbf{R}^5$ spanned by the column vectors of A'.

3. V, W are the real vector spaces of functions $\mathbf{R} \to \mathbf{R}$ with the respective forms $a + b \cos t + c \sin t$, $a + b \cos t + c \sin t + dt$ where $a, b, c, d \in \mathbf{R}$. $F : V \to W$ is defined by $F(f) = \int_0^t f \, dt$. Find the matrix associated with F relative to the bases $\{1, \cos t, \sin t\}$, $\{1, t, \cos t, \sin t\}$.

4. V is the real vector space of functions $\mathbf{R} \to \mathbf{R}$ of the form $a + b \cos 2t + c \sin 2t$ where $a, b, c \in R$. $F : V \to V$ is differentiation. Find the matrices A, B associated with F relative to the bases $\{1, \cos 2t, \sin 2t\}$ and $\{\cos^2 t, \sin^2 t, \cos t \sin t\}$ respectively.
   Verify that $B = T^{-1}AT$ where T is the matrix relating the bases.

5. (i) Show that the column vectors
$$[2i, 1, 0]', \qquad [2, -i, 1]', \qquad [0, 1+i, 1-i]'$$
form a basis for the complex vector space $\mathbf{C}^3$. Express $[1, 0, 0]'$ in terms of this basis.
   (ii) Find bases for the range and kernel of $L_A : \mathbf{C}^3 \to \mathbf{C}^3$ where
$$A = \begin{bmatrix} 1+i & 1-i & -2 \\ 1-i & -1-i & 2i \\ -1+i & 1+i & -2i \end{bmatrix}$$

6. V is the complex vector space of functions $\mathbf{R} \to \mathbf{C}$ of the form $a + b \cos t + c \sin t$ where $a, b, c \in \mathbf{C}$. $F : V \to V$ is differentiation. Find the matrix associated with F relative to the basis $\{1, \cos t, \sin t\}$. Use this matrix to determine the eigenvalues and eigenvectors of F. Can F be diagonalized?

7. In this question $\mathbf{C}^3$ is regarded as a unitary vector space in the standard way.

(i) Use the Gram–Schmidt process to construct an orthonormal basis for the subspace of $\mathbf{C}^3$ spanned by $[i, 1, 0]'$ and $[1, 1, 1]'$.

(ii) Prove that $L_A : \mathbf{C}^3 \to \mathbf{C}^3$ where

$$A = \begin{bmatrix} 0 & 3 & 0 \\ -3 & 0 & 4 \\ 0 & -4 & 0 \end{bmatrix}$$

is skew-hermitian.

Find an orthonormal basis which diagonalizes L_A and construct a unitary matrix U such that $U^{-1}AU$ is diagonal.

8. Find a Jordan basis for the linear operator $L_A : \mathbf{R}^3 \to \mathbf{R}^3$ where

$$A = \begin{bmatrix} -1 & 2 & -3 \\ 0 & 1 & -1 \\ 1 & -1 & 2 \end{bmatrix}.$$

Solve the simultaneous differential equations $dx/dt = Ax$.

9. $F : V \to W$ is a linear mapping. Prove that if kernel $F = \{O\}$ then F is *injective*, i.e. $F(v) = F(u)$ implies $v = u$. If F is also *surjective*, i.e. range $F = W$ prove that there is a unique linear mapping $G : W \to V$ such that GF, FG are the identity operators on V, W respectively (G is the *inverse* of F).

Deduce that if dim V = dim W and kernel $F = \{O\}$ then F has an inverse.

10 Express Problem 3.18(ii) as a problem on linear mappings and solve it by means of the theory of vector spaces (cf. Problem 6.12).

11. A, B are real symmetric $n \times n$ matrices and B is positive definite. Show that the definition $\langle x, y \rangle = x'By$ makes $\mathbf{R}^n$ into a euclidean vector space. Prove that $L_{B^{-1}A}$ is a symmetric operator on this space.

Deduce from Problem 6.20 that the real quadratic forms $x'Ax$, $x'Bx$ can be reduced simultaneously to diagonal forms.

Answers to Exercises

Chapter 1

1. $\begin{bmatrix} -9 & 6 \\ -6 & 6 \end{bmatrix}$, $\begin{bmatrix} -3 & -3 \\ 0 & 0 \end{bmatrix}$.

2. $B^2 - BA + 2B - I$.

3. The diagonal 3×3 matrices

5. $\begin{bmatrix} I & X \\ O & Y \end{bmatrix}$ where $X = \begin{bmatrix} -4 & -5 \\ 1 & 3 \\ 0 & -2 \end{bmatrix}$, $Y = \frac{1}{2}\begin{bmatrix} 3 & 4 \\ 1 & 2 \end{bmatrix}$.

Chapter 2

2. The determinant of an $n \times n$ skew-hermitian matrix is real or purely imaginary as n is even or odd.

3. $|A| = -6$. $\quad A^{-1} = \frac{1}{6}\begin{bmatrix} 3 & -3 & 3 \\ 1 & 1 & 1 \\ 1 & 1 & -5 \end{bmatrix}$.

4. $x_3 = -2$.

5. $(a-b)(b-c)(c-a)$; $\quad (a+b+c)(a-b)(b-c)(c-a)$;
   $(a-b+c)(a+\omega b+\omega^2 c)(a-\omega^2 b-\omega c)$ where $\omega = \exp(\pi i/3)$.

Chapter 3

1. (i) $x_1 = 2$, $x_2 = -3$, $x_3 = -2$, $x_4 = 0$.

2. (i) $\begin{bmatrix} 0 & 1 \\ 1 & 0 \end{bmatrix}$, $\begin{bmatrix} \alpha & 0 \\ 0 & 1 \end{bmatrix}$, $\begin{bmatrix} 1 & 0 \\ 0 & \alpha \end{bmatrix}$, $\begin{bmatrix} 1 & 0 \\ \beta & 1 \end{bmatrix}$, $\begin{bmatrix} 1 & \beta \\ 0 & 1 \end{bmatrix}$, $\alpha \neq 0$.

   (ii) $\begin{bmatrix} 1 & 0 \\ 3 & 1 \end{bmatrix}\begin{bmatrix} 1 & 0 \\ 0 & 5 \end{bmatrix}\begin{bmatrix} 1 & -1 \\ 0 & 1 \end{bmatrix}$.

3. (ii) One pair is $A = [1,0,1]$, $\beta = [0,1,0]$.

5. $-\frac{1}{2} \times$ given matrix.

Chapter 4

1. $T = \begin{bmatrix} 1 & -1 & -1 \\ 1 & 0 & -1 \\ 0 & 1 & 1 \end{bmatrix}$ is one choice. $x_1 = 1-e^{-t}$, $x_2 = 1$, $x_3 = e^{-t}-1$.

4. Particular choices are

(i) $\dfrac{1}{\sqrt{2}}\begin{bmatrix} -1 & 1 & 0 \\ 1 & 1 & 0 \\ 0 & 0 & \sqrt{2} \end{bmatrix}$ (ii) $\dfrac{1}{3\sqrt{2}}\begin{bmatrix} 3 & 1 & -2\sqrt{2} \\ -3 & 1 & -2\sqrt{2} \\ 0 & 4 & \sqrt{2} \end{bmatrix}$.

5. (i) $\begin{bmatrix} 0 & 2 & -1 \\ 2 & -1 & 0 \\ -1 & -1 & 1 \end{bmatrix}$ (ii) $\lambda^2 - \lambda$.

Chapter 5

1. One possibility is $y_1 = \frac{1}{2}(x_1 - x_2 - x_3 + x_4)$, $y_2 = \frac{1}{2}(x_3 + x_4)$, $y_3 = \frac{1}{2}(x_3 - x_4)$, $y_4 = \frac{1}{2}(x_1 + x_2 + x_3 + x_4)$ which reduces the form to $-y_1^2 - y_2^2 + y_3^2 + y_4^2$. The eigenvalues of A are $\frac{1}{4}(\pm 1 \pm \sqrt{5})$.

2. The given transformation is singular. Rank 2, index 1.

3. $(x_1 + x_2 + x_3 + x_4)(2x_1 + x_2 + 2x_3 + x_4)$.

5. (i) $\begin{bmatrix} 2 & 1 \\ 1 & 2 \end{bmatrix}$

   (ii) $R = \frac{1}{5}\begin{bmatrix} 4 & -3 \\ 3 & 4 \end{bmatrix}$, $S = 5\begin{bmatrix} 2 & 1 \\ 1 & 2 \end{bmatrix}$.

6. One possibility is $x = Ty$ where $T = \frac{1}{2}\begin{bmatrix} 1 & 1 & -1 \\ 1 & -1 & 1 \\ 0 & 2 & 0 \end{bmatrix}$. Max 3, min -1.

Chapter 6

1. Denote the given vectors by v_1, v_2, v_3. $\{v_1, v_2\}$ is a basis for W. $\{v_1, v_2, e_3, e_4\}$ is a basis for $\mathbf{R}^4$.

2. The first 3 columns of A and A' form bases for the subspaces.

3. $\begin{bmatrix} 0 & 0 & 1 \\ 1 & 0 & 0 \\ 0 & 0 & -1 \\ 0 & 1 & 0 \end{bmatrix}$.

4. $A = \begin{bmatrix} 0 & 0 & 0 \\ 0 & 0 & 2 \\ 0 & -2 & 0 \end{bmatrix}$, $B = \begin{bmatrix} 0 & 0 & 1 \\ 0 & 0 & -1 \\ -2 & 2 & 0 \end{bmatrix}$.

5. (i) $[1,0,0]' = -iv_1 - \frac{1}{2}v_2 + \frac{1}{4}(1+i)v_3$ where v_1, v_2, v_3 are the given vectors.

   (ii) $[1, -i, i]'$ forms a basis for range L_A. $[i, 1, 0]'$, $[1-i, 0, 1]'$ form a basis for kernel L_A.

6. $\begin{bmatrix} 0 & 0 & 0 \\ 0 & 0 & 1 \\ 0 & -1 & 0 \end{bmatrix}$.

   Eigenvalues 0, $\pm i$. Eigenvectors α, $\beta(\cos t + i\sin t)$, $\gamma(\cos t - i\sin t)$ where α, β, γ are arbitrary constants. Yes.

7. (i) $\frac{1}{\sqrt{2}}[i, 1, 0]'$, $\frac{1}{2\sqrt{2}}[1-i, 1+i, 2]'$.

   (ii) Orthonormal basis $\{v_1, v_2, v_3\}$ where $v_1 = \frac{1}{5}[4, 0, 3]'$,

   $v_2 = \frac{1}{5\sqrt{2}}[3, 5i, -4]'$, $v_3 = \frac{1}{5\sqrt{2}}[3, -5i, -4]'$.

   $U = [v_1 \, v_2 \, v_3]$. $U^{-1}AU = \mathrm{diag}\{0, 5i, -5i\}$.

8. $[1,1,0]'$, $[1,0,-1]'$, $[-1,1,1]'$ form a Jordan basis.
   $x_1 = -a + (b+c+bt)e^t$, $x_2 = a + (c+bt)e^t$, $x_3 = a - b\,e^t$ where a, b, c are arbitrary constants.

Index

Adjoint operator, 78
Adjugate matrix, 20
Augmented matrix, 28

C. C^n, 77
   standard basis, 77
   standard unitary structure, 77
Cauchy's Theorem, 22
Cayley–Hamilton Theorem, 49, 50, 72
Cayley's construction, 45, 53
Characteristic equation, 38
Characteristic polynomial, 42, 72
Cofactor, 19
Column vector, 1
Congruent matrices, 62
Coordinate vector, 69
Cramer's Rule, 22

Determinant, 14, 72

Eigenspace, 73
Eigenvalue, 38, 59, 71
   algebraic multiplicity of, 73
   geometric multiplicity of, 73
Eigenvector, 38, 59, 71
Elementary transformation, 27
Equivalence relation, 41
Euclidean vector space, 74

Gerschgorin's Theorem, 53
Gram-Schmidt process, 75, 79, 83

Hermitian
   matrix, 12, 44, 53
   operator, 78

Interchange, 14
Inverse matrix, 5, 35
Isometry, 46

Jordan basis, 80
Jordan normal form, 80

Kronecker delta, δ_{rs}, 5

Linear dependence, 65
Linear equations, 27
   consistency, 30
   non-trivial solutions, 31

Linear mapping(s), 68
   composition, 71
   kernel, 68
   matrix associated with, 69
   range, 68
   rank, 71
Linear operator, 71
   characteristic polynomial, 72
   determinant, 72
   eigenvalue, 71
   eigenvector, 71
   minimum polynomial, 72

Matrix, 1
   addition, 1
   characteristic equation, 38
   characteristic polynomial, 42
   circulant, 19
   complex, 1
   complex conjugate, 11
   determinant of, 14
   differentiation, 38
   echelon form, 27
   eigenvalue, 38, 59
   eigenvector, 38, 59
   elementary, 32, 34
   elementary transformation of, 27
   equality, 1
   exponential of, 52
   Jordan normal form, 80
   minimum polynomial, 49, 51
   multiplication, 2
   negative, 2
   non-singular, 21, 34
   normal form (under elementary
      transformations), 32
   order of, 1
   partitioned, 7
   polynomial, 49
   positive definite, 58
   rank, 29, 35, 67
   real, 1
   scalar multiplication, 6
   skew-circulant, 26
   square, 1
   square root of, 58
   stochastic, 42
   subtraction, 2
   trace of, 42

Matrix, *contd.*
  transpose of, 9
  unit, 5
  zero, 1

Minimum polynomial, 49, 51, 72
Minor, 21

Norm (of a vector), 43, 59, 75, 78
Normal
  matrix, 78
  modes, 61
  operator, 78

Orthogonal
  basis, 75, 78
  matrix, 43, 45, 47
  vectors, 43, 59, 75, 78
Orthonormal basis, 75

Permutation, 14
  even, 14
  odd, 14
Principal axes, 48

Quadratic form (real), 10
  definite, 57
  index, 55
  matrix of, 10
  negative definite, 55
  normal form, 55
  positive definite, 55
  signature, 55

R, R^n, 64
  standard basis, 67
  standard euclidean structure, 75
Row vector, 1

Scalar product, 42, 59, 74, 77
Similar matrices, 38, 41, 50, 51
Skew-hermitian
  matrix, 12, 44, 53
  operator, 78
Skew-symmetric matrix, 9, 18, 45
Symmetric
  matrix, 9, 45, 47
  operator, 75

Triangular matrix, 15

Unitary
  matrix, 43, 44, 53
  operator, 78
  vector space, 77

Vandermonde's determinant, 18
Vectors
  linearly dependent, 65
  linearly independent, 65
    maximal subset of, 65
Vector space
  basis, 66
  complex, 77
  euclidean, 74
  real, 64
  subspace, 65
  unitary, 77